STILL THE LIZARD

STILL THE LIZARD

TRANSFORMATION IS CLOSER THAN YOU THINK

STEVE SCANLON

RED LIZARD 🦎 PRESS

Published by: Red Lizard Press.

Library of Congress Control Number: 2017951862

ISBN 978-0-9970174-3-4

Still the Lizard / Steve Scanlon
Printed in the United States

CONTENTS

KNOW THYSELF

—The Oracle at Delphi

PREFACE

You have a lizard brain. I have a lizard brain. This part of the brain has been getting a lot of attention lately, and according to many scientists, it is the first part of your brain to evolve. It is called the lizard brain, or sometimes "reptilian brain," partly because of the proposed evolutionary aspect, and partly to indicate how this particular part of the brain functions. The lizard brain is crucial, and it is my hope that this book enlightens you as to why that is.

To say that technology has changed over the last twenty years is a staggering understatement. What we can now do with technology, and what it can do for us, is truly astounding—changing art, careers, entertainment, medicine, and really all of life as we know it.

As technology has changed, it has made previously unknown frontiers knowable, and this is certainly true when it comes to the science of the brain—perhaps the greatest unknown frontier of them all. The best neuroscientists admit that when it comes to understanding the brain, we are just beginning to scratch the surface—but even so, how much knowledge scientists have gained in the field is astounding. With our remarkable new research in neurobiology, for example, we are able to shine new light on the cognitive sciences in areas such as neuroplasticity, or the ability to affect change in our brains.

But since not everyone is a neuroscientist (or even a neuroscience-loving geek like me), I wanted to take what science is

1

discovering and make it accessible to a broad audience. And I decided to do that by telling the story of a character, Jake, who could easily be you or me. In Jake's story, you might not only see a little bit of yourself, but also discover some of the reasons that you do what you do. And perhaps you will also stumble upon why you don't do the things that you know you should.

It is my hope that this story resonates with you, and that with this resonance, you will begin to understand what science is discovering about the difficulty—and possibility—of human change.

This book was written especially for people who's lizard brain sometimes gets overactive. (Spoiler alert: that's all of us.)

THE EVENT THAT TRIGGERED IT ALL

THE ONLY JOURNEY
IS THE ONE WITHIN

— Rainer Maria Rilke

∗

A profound personal crisis sending him into total shock was not what Jake Davis had expected to experience that morning. He was sitting in a room full of fellow seminar attendees, listening to the latest, greatest ways to develop his business, his relationships, and his life, taught by yet another soul who'd found "the" way to be successful. Suddenly, life as he had lived it up until that moment seemed so pointless. What a waste of his time, his money, and his energies, he thought. And why should his life unravel right there in that room? Why now? But it had. And Jake would have to accept his life for what he now saw it was—headed straight for the kind of mediocrity he had sworn long ago to avoid.

Until that day, Jake had been a man with a passion. He was always reaching toward something. The pursuit of excellence, growth, and development was always on his mind. For years, he had been attending seminars and workshops—all of which taught the latest theories on time management, productivity, leadership, and wealth accumulation. He had read all the books on those topics, and a host of others besides. And yet, today he had realized that he was still the same old him—with the same old patterns, and same old habits—and that absolutely nothing about his life was truly different.

Nothing.

And if nothing had changed as a result of attending all those seminars, and all of that reading and studying, then what, exactly, had been the point of doing it? In a split second, Jake Davis went from being an eager participant in a leadership seminar to being a victim of an internal train wreck.

What a bizarre moment for this kind of realization. He tried to shake off the troubling thoughts and refocus, but he couldn't. In this room full of strangers, Jake had a very shattering, very private meltdown.

Why now? He tried to remind himself that he had good friends, a great family, many talents, and a life worth far more than just what he had been able to put in the bank. Still, the darkness descended. With every passing moment, he felt more and more engaged in a battle against himself.

In an effort to quash this inner crisis, Jake tried to recall the lessons he had learned, and the insight he had gleaned, from all of those books and seminars over the years. Certainly there must be something from all of that learning that could counteract this onslaught of self-doubt. He made an attempt to remember the various laws, strategies, and tactics that he had studied, hoping to find something—anything—that would bring him comfort, but it was useless. Nothing he had learned over the years seemed to help stifle the rising panic he felt inside, insisting that his life was just the same now as it always had been. Had he made any improvements at all? Did he think differently, act differently, or live differently? In that moment, the clear answer was, "No." *Enough of this*, he thought. *Enough. Get up and get out of here.* He sat up a little straighter and—with a calm that masked his inner turmoil—began gathering his things. He figured people would think that he had to leave due to an urgent issue at home or the office, but it didn't really matter what anyone thought. All he cared about at that moment was getting out the door, and away from this seminar—as if that would also separate him from the bleak fog that was rolling over him.

That fog was so thick, he wasn't sure he could even make it to the door. He had already begun swearing off all future seminars and books—anything that promised some type of personal or professional growth. He had also begun to blame all the teachers, speakers, and motivators. He was angry at himself for buying into the hope of a better life, but he was even angrier at the people who promised it. Either they didn't correctly teach their six simple steps (or however many steps, minutes, or whatever the latest theory-of-the-month proposed), or there was nothing of value to any of it in the first place. Jake suspected the latter.

He made his way to the back of the room, but paused briefly at the door. A tiny spark of curiosity managed to burn its way through the fog, and made him wonder what he would be leaving behind when he walked out of the room. He turned his attention back to the speaker just long enough to hear her say,

"And that, my friends, is what we call the lizard brain." *Huh*, Jake thought. *What in the world could that mean? I have no idea.* And he made his escape.

The walk to the car was strange. Jake felt numb, and mentally exhausted. His M.O. for coming away from a seminar always included having a notebook full of notes, and a head full of new ideas. In contrast, today felt like the beginning of a new journey—one that was void of any ideas at all. Jake felt empty.

He decided that his decision to leave in the middle of the seminar would be symbolic of a broader decision to leave his usual way of thinking behind. From now on, he would simply accept that there were some people who walked in the light (so to speak), and some who just walked in mediocrity. No more workshops, seminars, or courses for him. No more books from the personal development section of the bookstore. Or the business leadership section. Or the money management section. In fact, he would even swear off the do-it-yourself section, just to be safe. His wife would be pleased with that last one, he thought with a weak grin. No more plumbing repairs that never seemed to get completed, or half-finished furniture projects inspired by whatever DIY book had caught his eye. He wouldn't tell his wife about his experience today. How do you explain giving up on that many years of … what exactly? Trying to be better than you are apparently capable of being? And do you apologize for all the time and money that went into these things? Oh, he and Laurie were doing fine financially, and he spent a lot of quality time with her and the kids. But still, all that time, money, and everything else he had invested in this endless pursuit now seemed like such a total waste.

He sat motionless in his car and tried to convince himself he'd be better off without all the teachings and books—but the truth was that he simply felt empty. Drained. Spent. *Well, better that than embarrassment, or anger, or anything else,* he told himself. *I am what I am, apparently. And I will never be a superstar. So I will learn to embrace mediocrity.* He clung to the emptiness and drove home.

*

But Jake had once been much more than mediocre. He was a star player on his Little League baseball teams. And in high school, he was the hero of his team. He was a natural at baseball, and he loved the game. He accepted a sports scholarship to college, and even had his sights set on going pro. A farm club for a year at most, he thought, and then the Show. Then, in the middle of his sophomore year, star player Jake Davis blew out his knee. In a big way. In a get-addicted-to-painkillers-while-recovering kind of way. But Jake never talked about that, or about the two and a half years that followed. He rarely allowed himself to think about the injury, much less the addiction. He met Laurie during that bleak time, and she doesn't talk about the circumstances surrounding that time either. The physical recovery from his knee surgery was a harrowing experience, accompanied as it was by the loss of a dream. But the second, long recovery from addiction was worse, and it had shown the world a weakness that Jake was afraid of. But in the end, there had been a positive outcome. After all, it was the void left by baseball, and by his subsequent recoveries, that had caused him to channel his intense energy, and his pursuit for excellence, into other areas.

Jake jerked back to attention and realized he'd been staring blankly at his laptop for the last ten minutes. A month had passed since that fateful seminar, and as he got up from the desk in his office to stand by the window, he thought how odd it was to think about all of that ancient history now. He enjoyed thinking about his years playing baseball, and then of finally getting his degree in finance, marrying Laurie, the birth of his daughters, and everything else that had happened since. But he never allowed himself to think about that second recovery, and the time between baseball and the rest of his life. Funny, he'd never before connected his thirst for improvement to that difficult period in his life. But now that connection had been made, and he found himself wondering why—why was he thinking about it now, long after his decision to put it behind him?

He mused at how easy it was to leave all the learning behind, and just move ahead on autopilot. This, to him in that moment, was validation that all of his work and effort had been a waste of time. Slowly, though, Jake began to realize that he hadn't replaced the learning with anything of value. He had taken away the pain of futility, but he began to see that he had only replaced it with the pain of emptiness. There were even a few days when he almost felt despair.

What did he really want? Why couldn't he just be happy with who he was, and what he had? After all, he had Laurie, his two daughters, a good job with a leading wealth management firm, a nice house, and some vacations. He would frequently go through this mental list of the good things in his life, but none of it seemed to get him over the hump. He didn't even really know what the "hump" was. All he knew for sure was that he felt unchanged, in spite of all of the years and effort he spent trying to grow and improve, and that was about as bleak a feeling as he could think of.

His realization about the roots of his quest for more (more skills, more knowledge, more achievement, and more opportunities) made him curious, and he decided to look at those roots a little more closely. When the struggle required by his physical therapy, and the long months of drug rehab (he mentally stumbled a bit over that thought) no longer had a purpose, his intensity had turned elsewhere. Determined to make up for lost time with his studies, he poured all of his energy into getting his degree. And he admitted it—maybe some of his energy went toward trying to convince Laurie that he was no longer the disaster he had been when they first met. He succeeded at both goals, and after that it just seemed natural to continue down the road of learning more ways to do things better. But understanding where the emptiness had begun did nothing to combat the dismal fog that he now lived with, and he no longer knew what the "better" that he had been reaching for even was.

Overwhelmed by his memories, and struggling to breathe, Jake pulled himself back to the present, turned away from the window, and went back to his computer.

He stayed on this mental rollercoaster for what seemed like forever, though in reality it was only a few weeks. Occasionally something at work would prompt him to want to learn more, and to want to get better, but as soon as he had these thoughts, Jake would banish them by reminding himself just how devastating it was to try to change and yet come up short. He was often able to make changes that helped for a while—but all too quickly, he would revert to his usual patterns. Lasting changes? He was beginning to wonder if they were even possible. Better, he thought, to stay clear of the stable altogether, rather than to try yet again to get back on the horse.

Jake decided this feeling of emptiness was his new reality and convinced himself that he could ride on this train for the rest of his life. And he might have done just that—had it not been for the lizards.

JAKE, MEET THE LIZARD

THE WORST BULLIES
YOU WILL EVER ENCOUNTER IN YOUR LIFE
ARE YOUR OWN THOUGHTS.

—Bryant McGill

*

The acute pain Jake had felt immediately following the seminar had slowly become just a dull ache. Day after day, whether at work or at home, Jake felt as if he were just going through the motions. He still worked hard, and even began mentoring a new analyst who reminded him of his younger self—a little overconfident maybe, but hungry to perform, and eager to learn. In spite of that, and while also working on some new prospects, he was still able to be home most nights for dinner with the family. Maybe he was watching more TV in the evenings than he usually did, but he was keeping up with things at home, staying on top of weekend chores, and attending whatever recital/performance/game his daughters had going. Work was fine, home was fine—but something was missing.

He was pretty sure it wasn't noticeable to anyone else. Except maybe Laurie. His wife had always been a little too perceptive for his comfort, but right now she was focused on her own projects. Substitute teaching in special education classrooms, as well as keeping two teenagers on schedule, would be enough to keep anyone busy. She did seem to notice that he hadn't been reading as much; his nightstand was usually overflowing with books, but it was empty now. She occasionally looked at him as if she wanted to ask him what was going on—but she didn't, and he was thankful. What would he tell her?

In spite of the fact he now felt numb, Jake was also grateful for not having to feel the pain he felt the day of the "lizard seminar" (as he'd come to think of it), but that was about it. He had no desire to jump back into learning anything new.

Strangely, the "lizard brain" comment began creeping into his thoughts on a regular basis, although he had no context for it. Stranger still was the fact that Jake began to see lizards, well—everywhere. There was a pet lizard at the house of one his daughter's friends. A new terrarium display full of lizards appeared in the window of a pet store that he walked by on a regular basis. He noticed a lizard in the rocks outside his office building, another on a bumper sticker when stopped at a traffic light, one on a book cover in a bookstore, and yet another in a logo for a beverage. Television commercials, billboards, magazine covers, live lizards behind glass, rubber ones sold as cheap toys—it was getting absurd.

But the crowning moment of Jake's new lizard awareness came when he was singing along with a song on the radio in his car. It was an old song from the '70s—one he liked, but couldn't quite remember the words to. He muttered his way through the verses, and suddenly he was singing about lizards… *Wait… what?!?* Jake pulled his car off to the side of the road. He sat behind the wheel and waited incredulously for the refrain to come around again. He turned up the radio—and sure enough, the lyric was something about lizards flying through the air! Unbelievable. And now he was really curious.

Jake didn't think he believed in fate, or in receiving mystical messages, but he couldn't deny that it seemed like the universe—or God, or something—wanted to send him a message. But what was the message, exactly? Was he supposed to get a lizard? Was he supposed to notice something about lizards? He needed some direction.

He drove home on autopilot, the wheels in his brain spinning. Jake struggled to remember if he had anything he needed to be doing once he got home, and when nothing came to mind, he was relieved. The house was empty, and he went straight to his computer.

He didn't think that just running a search on the word "lizard" would result in much of anything pertinent to his quest, so instead, he searched the two words he heard as he left that seminar: "lizard brain."

What popped up on the screen took him completely by surprise. His search had garnered over four million results. This number astounded Jake, given that he hadn't even heard the term until his grand exit from all things self-improvement. And yet, here were countless articles, talks, and books on the subject of the lizard brain. He wasn't sure he wanted to continue his research. Focusing on new learning—at any level—left such a bad taste in his mouth that he was ready to get up and walk away. And he would have, had it not been for how the freakish spate of lizard sightings continued to spark his curiosity. Jake shrugged his shoulders. It probably wouldn't hurt to just take a look. He sat back in his chair, and began to read.

He soon realized that the lizard brain described a particular region of the human brain, though there was some debate about where this so-called lizard brain was actually located. Some scientists said that it was located in (or at least is part of) the limbic system. Others had it specifically targeted at the amygdala. Still others didn't have it as part of the limbic system at all, but rather put it towards the base of the brain, where it controlled the "fight or flight" response. And while most agreed that it was the first part of the brain to evolve, there was some debate over what the lizard brain designation actually meant.[1]

This was the very sort of thing that would have intrigued the old, "pre-realization" Jake. And when he became aware of that fact, he considered closing the search window. Continuing his self-education on this topic felt too much like the "learn and improve" path he had gone down before.

But he reasoned to himself—life wasn't throwing him clues about leadership, or improving his interpersonal skills, or mastering new laws of finance. Instead, it was throwing him lizards! And bizarre reptilian phenomena simply begged to be understood at a deeper level. So he kept digging.

He read an article that spoke in-depth about this prehistoric part of the brain and its varying functions. The information was intriguing, but also highly academic, and while Jake learned words like amygdala, limbic system, and neuroplasticity, he also tried to find articles that spoke about the lizard brain in simpler, less academic ways. Some of the research identified it as simply the part of the brain that deals with the fight or flight response. Others described it as the prehistoric way that the brain handles emotions.

Jake's initial attempt to learn about this lizard brain was somewhat confusing, but the lizard sightings were simply too frequent, and too odd, to ignore. And every time he thought about giving up, Jake would find another reference to the lizard brain in popular culture. On the search results pages, he found links to YouTube video clips from sitcoms wedged between scholarly articles discussing neurobiology and the latest in psychological research. And before he realized what was happening, he was neck-deep in trying to understand the importance of the lizard brain, and how it affected people.

The next few days followed a typical pattern. Get up, make coffee, check his email, read the paper, drag the girls out of bed, and help Laurie get them off to school. That was a major undertaking in and of itself. Every day, he was astonished once again at what two teenage girls required to move out the door in the morning: discussions about clothes, gathering homework, book bags, and cell phones, and texting friends they would be seeing in ten short minutes. He would then head to his office. Work itself was normal, filled with research for clients, meetings with team members, and a never-ending stream of phone calls.

At lunch, though, Jake would shut the door to his office and focus on learning more about the lizard brain. It had an allure he couldn't escape, despite the resolution he'd made against any more learning.

After about a week of intensive exploration of the subject, Jake had a "Eureka!" moment. He was reading an article about how the amygdala plays a role in learning. Specifically, the author was explaining how stress and survival instincts activate parts of a person's brain in such a way that he or she can't retain information, or apply new learning.[2] *Is it possible*, he thought, *that the reason I have failed to apply so much of what I have learned is because I suffer from some lizard affliction?* Jake laughed at the thought of discussing such an ailment with his doctor. But his curiosity was now fully piqued, and he doubled down on his research project.

Jake went back into full-blown learning mode for a couple of weeks after that. Much of what he read was highly scientific, and he found himself appreciating more the articles, papers, blogs, and books that explained the everyday function of the lizard brain, rather than the science behind it. The science was interesting, and he was able to understand a lot of it, but what really intrigued him was the practical application of this knowledge. He wasn't looking to become a neuroscientist. He just wanted answers. Answers about why he was seeing lizards everywhere. Answers about why the speaker made that comment as he left the seminar. Answers about why he felt so stuck, and unable to become a better version of himself.

Everything he was reading led him to an inevitable conclusion: it was his own lizard brain holding him back.

At that point, he turned his focus on his own behavior. If Jake had a lizard brain—and it appeared that everyone did—how did it manifest itself? He wanted to witness it in action in his own life.

Apparently, the lizard brain was one of the first parts of the brain to develop in humans in utero, and some scientists believed that it was also the first to evolve.[3] It was this evolutionary element that had people referring to lizards in the first place.

Jake didn't want to get caught up in biological anthropology, but instead stay focused on what having a lizard brain meant for him, today. According to what he read, it seemed the lizard brain had two sides to it: a good side, and a not-so-good side.

It wasn't difficult to understand that the most important job of our most primal brain was to simply keep us alive. This part of the brain actually had an amazing design. Survival was its primary function—and that, Jake figured, was a good thing. He realized his lizard brain got him dressed in the morning, locked his house, and looked in the rearview mirror when he was driving, all actions he might not have taken had he had to think about them using the parts of the brain that are supposed to rationally consider things.

What Jake couldn't figure out initially was—what was the dark side of this part of his brain? What could possibly be the reason for his lizard brain holding him back? How would that protect his survival? It seemed counter-intuitive. After all, wasn't change a necessary component to life? Jake pondered this question for a few days, all the while discovering the many ways that his lizard brain helped him. This new attentiveness, or "mindfulness" (as one psychological study referred to it), to things that were usually largely unconscious was interesting, but it still didn't fully answer his questions. Why, or how, was the lizard brain affecting him negatively? And why on God's green earth, Jake wondered, would the trainer have said what she had in that particular context at the seminar? Looking back, he now regretted leaving.

Jake realized he had returned to being a full-blown, card-carrying, completely-obsessed learner. Figuring out how his brain worked consumed him, and he began to devour books, articles, and publications on anything that would help him to understand the human mind. His pursuit now was different from previous pursuits in that Jake was less interested in the lizard brain as a general topic, and more interested in how the topic affected him personally. This was new. He had learned so many ways to manage and lead others, and to help them grow and improve, but he couldn't think of a time when his learning had led him to discover truths about himself. He had been learning steps, principles, and topics so as to simply know them, which he now realized must certainly have played a part in his failure to actually apply them.

So I have a lizard brain. As does every other person on the planet, apparently. Jake smiled to himself. *At least I'm not alone.*

And he recognized the lizard brain's involuntary functioning in the ways it helped him dress, drive, and even accomplish some tasks at work, like typing in a code so automatically that he always had to physically go through the motions before he could tell someone else what it was. But it wasn't until he really began to observe his lizard-like ways that he began to solve the mystery of how this vital, innate part of the brain also could be the primary hindrance to his growth.

Characteristic One

FAMILIARITY

Jake's first discovery about the lizard brain's dark side came as he began to realize just how regimented his life had become. Jake's car was giving him trouble, and one afternoon he dropped it off at the garage. Laurie was driving him home when he got a call from the mechanic. Apparently, he had let his car go unmaintained a little too long, and now would need not only new brake pads, but rotors as well. Jake winced when the mechanic told him the price, and looked at Laurie.

"Looks like I'll need a ride to work for the next couple of days."

"It shouldn't be a problem," Laurie said. "What about getting home after work?"

Jake said he thought he could probably hitch a ride with a friend from work who didn't live too far away. It would only be for a couple of days, after all.

The following morning, after the daily circus of getting the girls out the door, Jake headed out of the house only to see that his car wasn't parked in the driveway. It took about three worried seconds before he remembered that his car was at the shop. Before he could laugh at himself, Laurie was right behind him with keys in hand, ready to take him to work.

Jake thought about his first meeting of the morning, and began digging in his briefcase to review the documents he would be going over with the junior members of his team. He was absorbed by a section that he thought needed work when he looked up, and realized they were still going straight on Washington Street. Laurie had missed the turn.

"Where are you going?" Jake barked.

"To your office, of course."

"Why are you going this way?" Jake asked with astonishment.

"No particular reason." Laurie's voice was mild. She looked over her shoulder and changed lanes.

Jake felt himself coming unglued. Why wouldn't she go the same way he went? The way he always went. You know, the *logical* way? How could she possibly think this other route to his office was a good choice? The red light at Montrose always got traffic backed up, and going down 10th and around on Sims had to add at least a couple of miles. Had she not thought about it at all? Jake clenched his jaw, trying to keep these questions—and his growing agitation—to himself. But with every "wrong" turn, Jake's feelings of disbelief intensified, and began to morph into anger.

He could almost feel his skin crawling as his wife—his very intelligent and capable wife, mind you—took a ridiculously circuitous way to work.

And then it hit him. Not gently, like an afternoon breeze, but sharply, like a boxer's punch to the face.

Skin crawling? Really? Why was he so disturbed by this? Jake suddenly realized that his strong reaction to something pretty

25

innocuous was rather extreme, to say the least. In his mind, he had even begun to call his wife names. In an instant, Jake went from feeling judgmental and irate to feeling guilty that he had such a capacity for bitterness over something so small, and toward someone he loved so deeply.

As his anger dissipated, Jake happened to glance up and see a billboard for an insurance company. Sure enough, there was a lizard. He shook his head and wondered: could his overreaction have had something to do with his lizard brain?

Laurie dropped him off, apparently unaware of his inner emotional turmoil, and Jake leaned over to give her a kiss goodbye before getting out of the car. He rushed into his office and feverishly attacked his computer, looking for clues as to what just happened.

He began his search not knowing exactly what he was looking for. He went back in his search history and relocated the articles and papers he had originally found on the lizard brain. He quickly read things that spoke to the "fight or flight" concept, skimming over talk of the amygdala and other parts of the limbic system, until he came across an article on how the brain is wired, and how it always seeks the familiar. Familiarity, researchers found, was linked to survival, as familiarity required a minimal expenditure of energy. From there, he found an article that described how researchers can read a subject's pupils, and tell instantly (within 300-400 milliseconds) which item a person will choose, with that choice being based entirely on the natural preference for familiarity. In addition, the subjects defended their familiarity-based choice as objectively rational when questioned about it.[4]

The evidence was clear: the human brain clung to familiarity. He remembered his momentary confusion over the absence of his car in its usual place that morning. He was accustomed to seeing it there. And, of course, there was his complete meltdown over the different route his wife had taken to work. Curious to see just how objectively rational his reaction had been (and hoping it was at least a little bit justified), he mapped out both routes to check the mileage. He was surprised and a little embarrassed when he saw that it was a difference of less than quarter of a mile. But the real issue, he realized, was the fact that Laurie's route was not his regular route. It wasn't familiar enough for him to remain on autopilot.

Here, finally, was a clue about how his own brain was holding him back. While all things familiar weren't necessarily problematic in themselves, they could be limiting, preventing us from seeing or doing things in new ways. Doing the familiar on autopilot was easy. Everything else required effort.

Jake concluded that so many of the ways that he wanted to be a different person seemed good on the surface (like when he was in a seminar hearing about the latest and greatest ways to grow), but just underneath lurked his lizard brain, which was always scanning for the familiar in order to conserve energy and to minimize effort. He returned from seminars excited and enthusiastic to undergo great change, but he now saw that it hadn't taken long for his lizard brain to guide him back to the old, familiar ways. This was the closest thing he'd felt to a real aha moment in a long time.

He thought about an afternoon he'd spent on the golf course the previous week. A friend, who was a much better golfer than Jake, was trying to coach him on his swing. Jake made the effort to adjust his stance accordingly for the first couple of holes, but then naturally reverted to his usual, familiar swing. The new way just felt too different, too uncomfortable. And he remembered his daughter telling him the very same thing the night before. He and Laurie had been trying to convince Katy that learning to type properly would be a huge help to her in pretty much everything she did going forward. But the correct fingerings felt too different to her, and she quickly gave up in frustration. He then had to referee the spat that inevitably ensued when Kylee told her sister, with a tone of superiority, "It really isn't that hard." But Kylee also needed what was familiar, perhaps even more than her sister did. She had never adjusted easily to new people and places, and comfort only came with familiarity.

How fascinating to see all of this in light of the lizard brain, Jake thought. He told himself he would be on the lookout for all things familiar, for those places in his life where his patterns were too predictable. At what other times would he get upset when things changed? Jake's commitment at this point was just to be aware, not to take action. And as interesting as this exercise concerning the brain would turn out to be, little did he realize he had only glimpsed the tip of the iceberg.

Characteristic Two

BEING RIGHT ABOUT EVERYTHING

Jake continued to observe his own behavior, and that of the people around him, looking for patterns of familiarity. He was on a mission to catch himself clinging to familiar things. It wasn't easy, because he soon realized that familiar always felt right. Why would anyone intentionally do something that felt wrong? *Now there's an interesting question*, he thought. Is it possible that the answer to it would help him understand why change was so often unappealing?

One evening, Jake was sitting in the living room with Laurie and the kids. It was one of the rare times they were all home, without any sports practices, play rehearsals, or any of the other myriad activities that seem to take over a family with teenagers, and Jake was enjoying just being with his family. He had his laptop, and was continuing his research on the lizard brain while the rest of the family argued the merits and downsides of various contestants on their favorite reality TV show.

As Jake began to read an article on emotional intelligence, he found himself thinking instead about the cars he and his wife owned. Perhaps it was because he just spent more than five hundred dollars on his car. Or maybe it was because he was suddenly faced with the idea of two teenage drivers in the family when his daughters brought home the permission slips they needed a parent to sign in order to participate in driver's education at school.

He laughed a little to himself, because cars seemed to be a great means by which he could study his lizard brain—familiarity with how he normally drove to work, which radio stations he usually played, etc. It suddenly struck him that perhaps Laurie's car needed some work as well. How long had it been since she'd had her brakes checked? What about rotating the tires? And he was certain that it had been a while since her last oil change. He turned to her.

"Honey, how long ago was your last oil change?"

"I think it was a couple of months ago," Laurie said, her attention still on the television.

"It's been a lot longer than that," Jake insisted, certain she didn't remember correctly.

"No, Honey," Laurie said. "It was just five or six weeks ago. I remember because it was around your mother's birthday."

"I don't remember your taking it in, and I'm pretty sure it's due for at least an oil change." Even Jake could hear the change of tone in his voice.

"Jake," Laurie said, finally peeling her eyes away from the show and turning to him. "Trust me, I took the car in and it's fine." She held his eye for a moment longer, then turned her attention back to the television.

But Jake was sure she was mistaken, and set his computer aside. He made a beeline to the garage to look at the sticker on the windshield so he could prove to his wife that she was dead wrong. But he didn't find one. There was no sticker on her car displaying information about the last oil change, and the fact that it was missing surely proved that it had been too long. Jake marched back to the family room to insist to his wife that he was right.

What happened next seemed to happen more often than Jake cared to admit. Rather than proving his point and winning the all-important oil change debate, Jake only managed to escalate a discussion about car maintenance into a full-blown fight about trust. Laurie's claim that the sticker must have fallen off didn't mean anything, and Jake maintained his position that the car was in desperate need of fresh oil. In addition, Jake felt an acute need to win the argument. He simply "knew" that he was not wrong, and he absolutely had to find a way to prove it.

The evening was ruined. So much for family night. The girls (who had pretended not to hear) went up to bed. Laurie and Jake also went to bed, but fell asleep back-to-back, each using silence as a weapon to show that the other was wrong. Wrong about the oil, and even more wrong about the breach of trust.

In the morning, their anger had cooled enough for them to talk. The kids got off to school, and as Jake was heading out the door, Laurie said that she loved him. Then she threw out a question that normally would have sent Jake into a tailspin had he not been spending so much time thinking about his lizard brain.

"You know you don't always have to be right, don't you?"

Had she said this the night before, it would have just restarted the argument they were having, but somehow, this morning, Jake allowed the comment to sink in without reacting to it. As he drove away from the house, turning left off of Washington Street (of course), he wondered if he did, indeed, always need to be right. *No*, Jake thought. *There are plenty of things I know I am wrong about.* As he pulled into the office parking garage, he knew he had some morning meetings. But he decided to take a few minutes first to make a list of all of the things he knew he wasn't right about. He wanted to show Laurie that she was wrong about his need to always be right. Then it hit him. He was about to make a "wrong list" so that he could prove that he was right. *Good Lord*, he thought. *How ridiculous is that?* Was Laurie actually right? Did Jake have to win every argument? To always be right, every time?

He wondered if this could be another result of having a lizard brain. Did the inner reptile always have to be right? Too curious to put this thought aside, and still reeling a bit from the night before, Jake went to his office, canceled his first (thankfully non-critical) meeting, and went right to his expanding research project.

His theory that being in the right was a typical need of the lizard brain was supported by what he read. Jake stumbled upon an online book review describing one scientist's work stringing together study after study that showed humans' need to be right. Not a *want*, but a *need*. The scientist made the case that our belief in our own rightness served our basic survival.[5] And Jake thought that probably made sense for all living creatures, human or otherwise. Animals couldn't afford to be wrong about what they eat, or to take time to figure out whether another animal, higher in the food chain perhaps, was friend or foe. Other sources all indicated the same thing: the human brain was designed to be right. Always. Specifically the part of the brain that dealt with fight or flight—the lizard brain!

According to what he was reading, the brain was able to determine a "right" course of action faster by processing information in the limbic system,[6] of which Jake now understood the lizard brain was a part of. And the faster we process the information, obviously, the faster we can take action. If we cannot decide what to do, we do not act (whether it is to eat, get out of bed, or take any other action), and if we do not act, we may perish. Once we have processed and acted on information, Jake realized, then an assumption of correctness, or of being right, allows us to continue taking action, avoiding any psychological pain that would come from the idea that we have acted wrongly.[7]

So apparently, Jake thought, *we know we are not always right, but it seems like we only realize that fact when our brains are given a chance to spend some time with the situation.* Jake could think of things he'd done, and things he said that weren't right, but he could only think of them once they were past. What about in the present? What about when you are doing everything in

JAKE, MEET THE LIZARD

the moment to prove to your wife that she is wrong about her last oil change?

He now had another piece of the lizard brain puzzle. In addition to clinging to familiar ways, Jake (along with most of the rest of the world, he believed) always had to be right. He was eager to get home to tell Laurie about this new discovery. Would she even believe him, or would she think he was just trying to excuse himself for his recent bad behavior? He cringed at that possibility, but Laurie had been supportive of his current research. She had always been supportive of all of his efforts, but she said she recognized that this project was different. In fact, even more than merely being supportive, she was beginning to get involved in it herself. When they talked about the lizard brain she had begun to talk about it as if it were somehow an independent agent, acting under its own volition. Jake laughed out loud at the thought, imagining a little lizard sitting on his head, arguing for or against things. He'd seen plenty of movies with shoulder devils arguing with shoulder angels, but none with a lizard on someone's head. With that thought, he closed his internet search and went to his next meeting.

As the day went on, he tried to look for situations where he believed he was right when he was actually wrong. This proved to be harder than finding familiarity in his life, because Jake couldn't really find any places where he wasn't right. Even acknowledging the ridiculous arrogance of the presumption, he still felt that he was almost always right in his thinking and decision-making.

The next few days were interesting, to say the least. Jake was learning about his lizard brain, but still couldn't find a way to see himself as being "wrong" at any given moment. About the only thing he felt he could do with this new information was to look for the little arguments in his life. Not the big ones about religion, politics, or morality, but the little ones—like oil changes, or how the girls studied (did they really need to wear earbuds?), or which toppings to have on pizza. Could he actually catch himself trying to fight for things that didn't matter? Or, at least, the issues that didn't actually warrant a fight?

Jake began to practice asking himself a different question. "Am I right or am I wrong?" wasn't an effective question for him, because, according to his lizard brain, it only ever had one answer. Instead, he began to ask himself, "Do I have to be right, or do I want peace?" Sometimes that question turned into, "Do I want to be right, or do I want to have good relationships?"

In addition to finding familiarity all over the place, Jake added "having to be right" to his list of things to search for. And armed with his new questions about being right versus having good relationships, suddenly he found his need to be right everywhere. He was thankful that the process of discovering his lizard brain in action was a private one, for if other people saw the things that Jake was seeing about himself, he believed it would mean social disaster.

Jake wasn't trying to fix anything about himself. He wasn't sure he'd know how to, anyway. He was still just taking baby steps at seeing his lizard brain at work. He knew that he might never solve the familiarity problem, or the "must-be-right" problem, but it began to be a game in his mind to witness them in action in his own life. One interesting by-product of identifying places to not engage in a fight was free time. Jake couldn't believe how much time and energy went into having to be right all the time. He often complained, especially at work, that he didn't have enough time. He wondered—if he were able to put aside the need to prove his rightness, how much time could he get back? This knowledge would save him in countless ways in the future, but today he was just pleased to have identified these two parts of the lizard brain. However, he soon discovered there was still more to it.

Characteristic Three

GOOD AND BAD HABITS

When Jake awoke one Saturday morning, he lay in bed and immediately began to consider these two new ideas about how his own brain was wired. He acknowledged to himself this wasn't really new—that in fact, his brain had been this way all along, and he was only just now seeing it. He marveled at the addictive nature of learning. It was something he had sworn off just a few weeks earlier, yet it had trapped him again. Here he was, not even fully awake, lying in his bed, on a weekend no less, thinking about his lizard brain and wanting to know more about it. For a brief moment, he considered returning to his previous plan—the one that included no more attempts at self-improvement. But his curiosity was now too strong to fight. So he let the river of ideas continue to flow.

Familiarity was everywhere in his life. How he got up every day, how he showered, and even how he did little things like brush his teeth and shave—all were overwhelmingly familiar. Most weren't bad or harmful in any way, but they all gave a clue as to how patterned his behavior was. Jake wondered if keeping to these patterns ever held him back. What hadn't he done as a result of his need for familiarity?

Being right about everything was an entirely different issue, as far as Jake was concerned. Familiarity with things was easy to spot, and usually not so emotionally charged. Catching himself wanting to be right in everything was different—it was almost painful. Laurie and the kids were proving to be a great testing ground for this, and he silently tried a couple of times a day to be aware of his "I'm-always-right-about-everything" nature. Something that morning told him that catching himself in the middle of needing to be right was not going to be easy.

That thought startled him. *Don't I already have enough to handle, what with the girls, and work? Do I need to add this struggle as well?*

Lying in bed, just letting the thoughts flow without trying to direct them, he had another unnerving thought. If it had been his own lizard brain holding him back from growth, then Jake had no one else to blame. Not the instructors, the books, or the curricula. The idea that his plans and dreams had been undermined by his own thinking was a bit too much, so he consciously pushed the notion aside. It was way easier—and frankly, felt better—to blame others.

Jake threw off the covers. It was Saturday morning after all, and Jake had made some promises to his family that weekend. He decided to focus on those instead of seeking any more discoveries about the lizard brain. He got up, made coffee, read the paper, and looked at his e-mail on his phone. Just the normal routine. He didn't think anything of it until Laurie joined him in the kitchen, and made an offhand comment about Jake's incessant habit of checking his e-mail.

Normally, these comments from Laurie came and went without his taking much notice. But Jake was now more attuned to how his brain was working, and his reaction to Laurie's "addicted to e-mail" comment surprised him. Rather than making his usual, automatic denial, he got curious.

"What do you mean by that?" Jake asked, trying hard not to sound defensive.

"Well," Laurie replied as she stirred milk into her coffee, "you wake up and check your e-mail, you check it during breakfast almost every morning, you check it again before you take a shower, I see you look at your phone before you get into your car, and you check it again, multiple times, when you come home from work. You even looked at it when we were out to dinner the other night, and," she said with a smile, "I'm pretty sure you were reading it in church on Sunday."

With every fiber in his soul, Jake wanted to lash back at what felt like an attack, but he caught himself. There were two thoughts that stopped him: the first was that he was committed to observing his desire to always "be right," and the second was that Laurie's tone and demeanor were not aggressive in any way. She was simply making an observation, not trying to attack him.

Did he, in fact, have an e-mail habit? Jake sat silently at the kitchen table, trying to convince himself that a habit was better than an addiction. And that word, of course, took him back to college and the days of the painkillers. Painkillers. Jake paused on the word, and he was distracted for a moment by the thought that often, painkillers eventually caused more pain than they killed. What a time in his life—and one better left in the past.

But the e-mail habit was happening right now, and he had to be honest and admit that he did, indeed, habitually check his e-mail. And then his mind made a sudden, random connection. Could habits have anything to do with the lizard brain? Was this yet another piece of the puzzle?

Jake went straight to his computer and began to search for more clues as to what was happening in his own mind. It certainly didn't take much digging to discover that the lizard brain loved habits. The articles on this subject were so abundant that Jake had trouble taking in all the headlines: "How to Break Habits," "How to Start New Habits," "The Science of Habit Maintenance."

This was definitely the lizard brain. In article after article, Jake read about how habits were critical to survival.[8] And as Jake had been learning, survival was the lizard brain's main focus.

Jake began to understand not only why the human brain longed to create habits, but also how very many habits he himself had. Laurie's comment about his habit of constantly checking e-mail was not only accurate—but, as it turned out, just the beginning of what he would learn about himself. From the way he chopped vegetables, to where he sat in church, to the television shows he "couldn't miss"—these were all things he did habitually, but none of which he'd ever seen as being a habit. It was, of course, easier to see habitual behavior in others, and even that was illuminating. He had never really noticed it before, but whenever they got coffee to go, Laurie always lined up the seam in the sleeve with the seam of the coffee cup before she took her first sip. And Kylee had a habit of patting the side of her purse as she put it on her shoulder, though he didn't know why. He could point to Katy's habits as well, and those of his coworkers, and every time he noticed someone else's, it brought to mind more of his own.

Certainly not all of these lizard-brain-managed, habitual actions were bad. In fact, Jake began to see most of his habits as neither good nor bad, but rather the rhythm by which he—and everyone else, for that matter—lived life. Many of the studies he read on habits pointed to the fact that they were, in fact, necessary. The brain, Jake learned, had to make habits because it simply could not make decisions about every minute detail of life. It would be far too overwhelming.

Jake began to pay particular attention to the habits that he knew weren't good for him, Laurie, or the kids. It would be unrealistic for him to try to keep track of all of his habits, but he could home in on a few that seemed to be holding him back. He even learned some current theories on the best way to create new habits, but that felt too much like attempting growth. Right now he was simply information-gathering to continue to learn about his lizard brain. Maybe one day this knowledge could be used to bring about change in his life, but today, the information alone was all Jake wanted.

Characteristic Four

CONTROL

Jake discovered the fourth—and what turned out to be the final—characteristic of the lizard brain on a rainy Sunday afternoon in March. Much like the discovery of the other three characteristics, this one came without warning, and was both unwelcome and uncomfortable.

Life continued as normal. The kids were busy with school, Laurie was engaged in her daily activities, and Jake continued his back and forth to the office. Meetings, conference calls, new business, and old business—all seemed to be going well. The reality of the mental breakdown at the conference was still there, and he knew that at some point he would have to face it, but overall Jake was okay. For now, he was content to go through the daily motions, and to continue to look for his lizard brain at work. Familiar patterns presented themselves to him more regularly. He still had disagreements with colleagues at work, and sometimes with Laurie and the kids, but he was developing an ability to catch himself wanting to be right. And identifying his habits had begun to be a kind of game. Sometimes the game was fun, and sometimes not, but it was always enlightening, and Jake figured that even just playing the game was a step in the right direction.

The next discovery started as Jake was traveling to Oklahoma City to meet prospective clients, and to take them through his

43

firm's products and processes face-to-face. The meeting had been set up by his CEO, who then proceeded, in a series of e-mails, to remind Jake how crucial the meeting was. As if Jake wasn't already aware how important this deal was to himself, his CEO, and his company.

On the way to Oklahoma, Jake had a layover in Denver. As luck (or fate) would have it, the Denver area was hit with a sudden and violent storm that shut down the airport. His flight was one of the last to land, and it soon became clear that nobody was going anywhere that night. Period. He would not be getting to Oklahoma City before his eight o'clock meeting the next morning.

As he stood in line at the customer service counter in Denver, he felt an unbelievable amount of agitation. Or was it frustration? Anxiety? Whatever you wanted to call it, it was bad. There was simply no way to get to that early meeting the next day. Jake wanted to start yelling. The long wait in line with other aggrieved passengers was not helping his mindset. As his level of frustration and anxiety grew, he could feel himself wanting to berate the hapless service representatives at the counter. There was a small voice of reason reminding him that the poor agents had no control over the weather, but it was drowned out by the much louder voice of indignation, telling him how outrageous this was. He felt so out of control.

The next morning, in the hotel by the airport where he'd spent the night, Jake tried to understand what had happened the evening before. As he considered his behavior, he felt as if he'd held it together pretty well. His intense agitation was mostly internal—his jaw had been clenched while he was speaking to the agents, but at least he hadn't raised his voice. But something inside him wondered if his reaction might have had something to do with the lizard brain. After all, it was laughable that something like bad weather causing him to miss a flight would trigger such an intense reaction in him. Surely something else must be going on.

Could it have something to do with wanting to stay in a familiar routine? Was there something about the previous evening at the airport that had created a scenario in which he knew he was "right?" Perhaps a little. Still, this was different, somehow. His frustration wasn't anything to do with habits. Maybe he was stretching to try to make everything about the lizard brain; maybe this situation had nothing to do with it at all. And yet, Jake's emotional state had carried him to the brink of seriously losing his cool in a public place—something that might have felt good in the moment, but would inevitably have brought shame later.

He sat in the hotel room and silently reviewed the facts of the night before several times. Jake was stunned (and a little ashamed) that his reaction was so inconsistent with who he thought he was. And then it came to him: he had felt so very out of control. He could do nothing to manage the weather, the air-traffic controllers, or the slick runways. He had no say in grounding air traffic, or when that decision would be reversed. He couldn't control missing the meeting that was so important, and because his flight cancellation had been so late, there had been no one to call to explain.

It made him wonder. In addition to familiarity, being right, and habits, was being in control also something the lizard brain longed for? He looked at his watch. *Another couple of hours before the rescheduled flight*, Jake thought. *May as well search this.*

Like the other characteristics of the lizard brain, being in control was easy to research. Jake found an article making reference to Maslow's Hierarchy. He remembered from his college psych class that Maslow's Hierarchy stated that we seek to control the bottom section of the hierarchy first, and then work our way up in succession as each part comes under our control. The article went on to say that once a given part of the hierarchy is under our control, we don't notice it as much. It's only when parts of the lower sections move out of our control that we perceive a threat to our survival.[9]

For Jake, this confirmed that what he had so fully experienced the night before was an example, live and in Technicolor, of how we react when our lizard brains feel out of control. The lizard brain does not like the feeling, and will go to some pretty extreme measures to make sure we stay firmly in the driver's seat in order to ensure our survival. And while in this case his physical survival hadn't been threatened, his lack of control over his situation had triggered a strongly negative response nonetheless.

Once he was settled on his morning flight to Oklahoma City, he realized how ridiculous his reaction had been, in the end. When the clients in Oklahoma learned about the storm, being reasonable people, they simply moved the meeting to the afternoon, and Jake made it in plenty of time. The meeting went great, and Jake felt like he was able to build a good working relationship with the clients, and their team. Though not without a few frustrated e-mails from his CEO, which Jake now realized were his boss's own response to feeling out of control over the meeting.

Jake wondered how often he, and everyone he knew, suffered from overreacting when not feeling in control. How many nasty e-mails were sent? How many angry words were uttered, just because we felt out of control? How many situations were made so much worse than they really needed to be? The lizard brain strikes again, he thought.

On his flight home that evening, he tried to summarize for himself what he had been learning over the last few months. The lizard brain, as far as Jake could understand it, had four key characteristics:① it looked for *familiarity*,② it always wanted to *be right*,③ it longed to develop *habits* (good or bad) and④ it desperately wanted to be in *control*. As he considered his reactions to various situations in his life, and the reactions of the people around him, he realized that he could almost always identify at least one of those four characteristics at work. And with these four items clearly defined for himself, Jake felt that his understanding of the lizard brain was complete.

This is enough, he thought. Enough to keep him busy for a while, at least, and he made a commitment to be on the alert for the ways these characteristics manifested themselves in his life. It was clear that the lizard brain was not just a theory, and it wasn't just his own personal experience. Rather, it was reality that everyone experienced, because he and about seven billion other people on the planet had a lizard brain. For a brief moment, he was comforted by his new understanding. But the feeling was not to last.

A SECOND DARKNESS

LIFE IS UNDER NO OBLIGATION
TO GIVE US WHAT WE EXPECT.

—Margaret Mitchell

*

More than a month had passed since Jake's trip to Oklahoma, and everything was going well with the new clients. The girls were in their last month of school for the year, the family was beginning to discuss summer plans, and it had gotten easier for Jake to see his own lizard brain at work.

Realizing the many places where habit played a role no longer surprised him. Needing to be right still plagued him on an almost daily basis, but he was getting better at recognizing the situations as they happened, instead of after the fact. Familiar patterns were everywhere, and, though they were easy enough to spot, he noticed that he still went back to them simply because they "felt good."

Thankfully, Jake didn't feel out of control very often, so he didn't really feel like he had to deal with the lizard brain's desire to be in control. But then this, too, began to bother him. His controlled, little life felt like just that—controlled and little. Jake assumed that this was better than living out of control, but sometimes he wondered if the desire to be always in control wasn't holding him back somehow. (From what, he didn't know.)

Jake sat brooding over his coffee at the kitchen counter, reliving the past few months of his life. As uncomfortable as it was to remember "meltdown day" at the seminar, Jake found himself thinking about both that morning, and the subsequent journey that had brought him to his current understanding of how his brain worked. *Or sometimes didn't,* he thought.

He had been dogged in his attempts to understand the lizard brain, and he felt some satisfaction in that. But where, in the end, had it brought him? Was he any better for it? Did all this learning about the brain help him better understand past failures? Did it address his inability to change in some sustainable way? Did it bring him any more peace than before? Was he somehow more successful? Or was it just more knowledge for its own sake? Had all the research been in vain? So he now had this newfound knowledge that people have a lizard brain, and he had even gotten pretty good at seeing his own in action. *So what?*

And with that last thought, Jake slipped back into the dark fog, this time with his lizard brain in tow. He felt empty. Again. It was as if he were right back in the middle of that seminar and he stood, ready to walk out all over again, to leave it all behind as he did before. That's when the bleakness really hit. There was nowhere to go.

So Jake sat back down, staring at some crumbs on the counter, wishing that his pressing desire to learn and grow would simply fade, forever this time. There may have been something to this lizard brain thing, but right now it felt empty and meaningless. What was the point? Another theory learned that would ultimately prove useless.

Jake closed his eyes and slouched on his stool in the kitchen, while his mostly untouched cup of coffee went cold. He prayed that these demons would relent, and that eventually he would find what he was looking for. But in this new, second darkness, he had no idea what that was. He felt like he was in an endless maze, with no way out. The room around him grew small and dark.

A CRACK OF LIGHT

You can cut all the flowers but you cannot keep Spring from coming.

—Pablo Neruda

*

Church was as good a place as any to find some respite. Jake and Laurie had been attending for years, and went with the girls almost every Sunday. But the truth was that Jake wasn't what anyone would call "attentive" to the service. Sure, he went, and sometimes he even listened, but more often than not he was lost in other thoughts. Lately, those thoughts had been about the lizard brain, but work and sports—football or baseball, depending on the season—featured regularly. He and Laurie had talked a little about this, but Jake reasoned that it was enough that he was attending, and both of them thought it was good for the girls.

This particular Sunday, the pastor was speaking about the early years of Christianity, and said something about how those first churches needed to be different than the culture around them. The idea of needing to be different caught Jake's attention, and he found himself following the message a little more closely than usual.

As the pastor spoke about the Apostle Paul going from town to town, encouraging the people in the new Christian faith, Jake wondered what it took for those people to make such a monumental change to a new religion. He even wondered if there hadn't been a first-century version of himself—someone who longed to change, but couldn't. This thought sent him down a rabbit hole. To amuse himself, he imagined an ancient Greek version of himself, and toyed with the idea of how this old-world Jake would have handled the seminar, and the soul-searching that came after. What form would the lizard brain have taken in the ancient world? Always needing to ride the same donkey to market? Jake coughed to smother a laugh.

He was totally distracted from the sermon, and very amused by his own thoughts, when the pastor's words yanked him back to the present. The pastor was saying something about not conforming to the pattern of the world, and then transforming by renewing one's mind.

Jake missed exactly what had been said, so he leaned over and, in a whisper, asked Laurie for the reference, hoping that she had been paying closer attention. Laurie looked at her husband half in frustration, half in sympathy, and then pointed to the notes she had been taking: *Romans 12—transform our minds.*

And there it was. Could this be the answer he'd been looking for? He had to laugh at himself as he thought that he had never had an epiphany in church before. He'd better not tell anyone that. He took the Bible from the back of the pew in front of him, and looked up Romans 12: "Do not conform to the pattern of this world, but be transformed by the renewing of your mind." Sure enough, this verse spoke to him as clearly as if it were a sign.

Jake knew in that moment that the time he'd spent learning about the lizard brain had not been wasted. He had already realized that his lizard brain had too much control in his life, but now he knew that if he were to ever come fully back to the land of the living he would, indeed, have to be transformed in his mind. And he would have to find a way to lessen the effects of his own lizard brain, if he wanted to have any hope of transformation.

His first thought was to kill his lizard brain—but he didn't think he should, even if he could. The lizard brain wasn't all bad. In fact, based on everything he was reading, it was necessary for survival.[10] After all, it came with the original design, and ultimately, it was there to protect him. But was it supposed to rule his life? Anyone's life? Jake vacillated back and forth between the question of how to deal with his lizard brain and the pastor's voice, giving a message that he thought was intended directly for him. In a moment of guilt, he wondered how many other messages were intended for him that he hadn't heard, because of how insistent his lizard's voice was.

His thoughts were racing. As the church service began drawing to a close, he decided to figure out how he could stop the lizard brain from ruling his life, once and for all. Since killing this part of the brain was not a practical option, he tried to come up with a word that would be more constructive than "kill." Then it hit him. *If I can't actually kill it*, Jake thought, *perhaps I can at least still it*. That was it! Don't kill it, still it!

And right there, Jake had a new mission—still the lizard.

He didn't remember the end of the sermon, or the closing hymn. The phrase "still the lizard" kept repeating itself in his head. Jake remembered the movie *Field of Dreams*, where the main character kept hearing the voice telling him to build a baseball diamond in his cornfield. "Go the distance. Ease his pain." Jake smiled to himself as he added, "Still the lizard." Jake began to feel that finally he had found an answer to his question about what was the ultimate point of learning about the lizard brain. He now knew the purpose of all of his seeking.

LIZARD, MEET JAKE

LIFE DOESN'T GET EASIER OR MORE
FORGIVING, WE GET STRONGER
AND MORE RESILIENT.

—Steve Maraboli

STILL THE LIZARD

✳

Jake was quiet on the way home from church. While the girls laughed together in the back seat, he could see Laurie watching him. He wondered if she was seeing something in his face. After a minute or two, she spoke.

"What are you thinking about?"

"I think I may have figured something out at church," Jake replied, half hopeful, half amazed.

"At church? Really?" She smiled at him. "You mean you were actually listening to the sermon?"

"Yeah." Jake laughed back. "Okay, maybe not the whole thing. But the part about not conforming to how the world operates, and instead being transformed in our minds really hit me."

He felt a little embarrassed to tell Laurie that he was about to make a new commitment to learning about neuroscience based on a passage in Romans 12, but he had already talked to her about the lizard brain, so why feel that way? And Jake was excited enough about the possibilities he saw to want to share them with his wife.

He began to speak slowly, stumbling over his disorganized thoughts, but his excitement grew as he continued, and he could see that Laurie was getting as caught up in the idea as he was.

She asked questions, and began to think out loud with him about what renewing one's mind might look like.

He had done enough study on the lizard brain to know that it was real, and he had done enough observation of his own behavior to know that the lizard brain was powerful. But it controlled too much of his life—it was too dominant, and too active—and now Jake was determined to take some of that control back.

Later that afternoon, Jake went out for his weekly long run, and he found himself wondering how he might go about this process of stilling the lizard. What he needed to do was crystal clear, and why he needed to do it was equally obvious. But "how?" was the question.

Jake wondered how, since the lizard brain always insisted on being right, one could ever truly transform. You would have to acknowledge that some, if not almost all, of your thinking was wrong! If the lizard brain's job was to look for familiarity, to always be right, to make habits, and to control everything, then no wonder it was so difficult to still it. Even just trying to do so was going to seriously challenge every one of the very powerful characteristics of the lizard brain.

Good God, Jake thought. *No wonder so few people actually do this*! If most people couldn't learn to still their lizard brains, then positive change—at least any but the most temporary of changes—would be extremely difficult. It must be like going to war with your own instincts! He remembered the quote from Will

Rogers: "People change. But not much." He tried to remember other quotes on change, but the only thing that came to mind was, "You can't teach an old dog new tricks." For a moment, Jake felt a tinge of despair. If people don't change, and there are no new tricks for old dogs, then what's the point of even trying?

But a question nagged at his consciousness: why would there be a command to transform our minds if there were no possibility of actually doing so? And a Biblical command, no less! Jake reasoned that there'd be no value to Christianity in the world, or any other religion for that matter, if people couldn't change. If they could do it in the first century, then it could be done now. Will Rogers, Jake concluded, was only half right.

The phrase from the sermon about "transforming your mind" kept running through his head. If you can still the lizard, you can transform the mind. Or was it the other way around? If you transform your mind, will you then still the lizard? The circular thinking was beginning to give him a headache. But it was also giving him fuel for his new mission—one that was less about external factors, and more about learning how to effectively change his thinking.

Jake realized that his personal holy grail had morphed from understanding the lizard brain comment from his last seminar, to learning about the lizard brain and its individual characteristics, to fully grasping how to quell its effects. He decided that if he could just still his inner lizard, then he could be transformed in his mind, and this would be the key to finally having the peace, freedom, and authentic success he had been chasing his entire adult life.

As he cooled down at the end of his run, he found his thoughts right back where they started. So how, then, could he still the lizard? Perhaps the best way to still it was to prevent it from having such a strong voice in the first place.

Strategy One

REST
The Power of a Brain That Pauses

Monday morning, Jake lay in bed after turning off his alarm, struggling as usual to wake up all the way. His first thoughts were about how to tackle his lizard brain, but he couldn't muster any enthusiasm. All he felt was tired. Though Jake had gone to bed excited about his new goal of learning ways to "still it, not kill it," he simply couldn't get to sleep. Perhaps, he thought, it was because he had gone to bed with his mind racing. In any case, he had woken several times during the night wondering where this new journey might take him. It was not a good night's sleep. That itself wasn't out of the ordinary—Jake often experienced insomnia over worries about work issues, or challenges with the girls or Laurie.

More awake now, he thought about why he had woken up so many times during the night, and specifically the feeling of dread that came over him each time. He had found himself wondering if the transformation would alter him so much that he would become a whole new person. And what if no one liked that new person? What if his family liked him better as he was now, active lizard brain and all? He was a little embarrassed by these demons that had taunted him in the wee hours of the night. What had been so real and so alarming at 3:00 in the morning now seemed ridiculous. Jake laughed at himself as he swung his feet to the floor. He got up and plodded to the bathroom.

By the time he went downstairs, Kylee and Katy were already loading their backpacks for school. Jake walked past them before his brain registered what he saw: Kylee's top was too snug for his peace of mind as a father. After pausing for what he would later realize was a much shorter amount of time than he should have, Jake told her in his sternest voice that her shirt was far too small, and she looked terrible. She absolutely needed to change before she left for school.

He couldn't believe Laurie hadn't said anything about it. She was standing right there at the counter with her cup of coffee. But his wife apparently didn't have any issues with how Kylee was dressed, because she immediately jumped in to defend her daughter. Kylee was now teary-eyed, but Laurie comforted her, smiled, and sent both girls out the door before turning back to Jake with an expression that he, unfortunately, was all too familiar with. And suddenly it was the oil change argument all over again—no longer about T-shirts or car maintenance, but rather about trust, judgment, and sensitivity. He quickly realized this was a battle that he was going to lose, so he mumbled something about finishing the discussion later, and headed out the door.

By the time he was in his car, Jake had cooled down enough to recognize the lizard brain's role in what had happened. But identifying the lizard brain at work was part of the old journey, not the new. Learning about the characteristics of the lizard brain was one thing, but learning *why* it came into play at any given moment was quite another. This "why" was a far more challenging question than "what." Why did the lizard brain plague him in that moment? Jake wanted to understand, but it was so difficult to see beyond his own visceral reaction. This time, he thought, he truly *was* right. It was the wrong moment to ask why the lizard brain had been triggered, because it felt so right for it to have been triggered in the first place! He was thinking in circles again, he realized, and once again felt exhausted as he started the car.

As he paused at the first stop sign, Jake had a thought: *what if I cannot come to any conclusion about this simply because of how tired I am?* Another thought followed close behind it: *what if the lizard brain is louder when we are tired? Is this part of my brain stronger when I am worn down by exhaustion?*

This was a new concept. Does fatigue put the lizard on steroids? *Definitely something to research further*, Jake thought. He knew beyond a shadow of a doubt that his run-in with his daughter was due, in part, to his desire to be right—not to mention his need to control his family. But until now, he hadn't considered that his quick reaction (and perhaps overreaction) had been due to the fact that he was sleep-deprived.

Jake knew he hadn't slept well the night before, and he remembered reading something about the importance of sleep in many of his studies about the functioning of the brain. In fact, now that he thought about it, sleeping and resting had come up often. Up to this point in his journey, however, Jake had simply glossed over it.

Thank God the lizard brain knows how to drive a car, Jake thought. His mind was not on the drive, but on the scene at home, the insights that followed, and whether or not he had time to swing through a drive-through for an expensive and potent cup of something that would help him wake up a little more. Jake began to wonder if he was tired too often, because he knew where every coffee shop was on his route to work, and which was likely to have the shortest line in the drive-through.

Good Lord, Jake thought, picturing the usual long lines at Starbucks in the morning. *We do need our caffeine.* This was a particularly sobering thought. It shed light on his own caffeine habit, but he had also thought the word "we" and not "I," making him realize he was by no means alone in a very coffee-dependent world. He paused briefly to consider recommending Starbucks as a stock purchase—*SBUX on the NASDAQ, right?* From that point on, the questions came pouring into his mind. How often did he not get enough sleep, and how much of his life was spent unrested? Jake began to think of all of the things that people used to keep awake. As well as different kinds of coffee, there were so many energy drinks that they required their own aisle in the grocery store. The whole world seemed to need a lot of energy. Was it because we no longer got enough rest?

By the time Jake sat down in his office, he realized it was easier to count the people *without* coffee cups in hand than it was to count those *with*. So he decided to ask a few of his colleagues about how much rest they got, and what they said shocked him.

Just about everyone he spoke to at work reported that they didn't get enough sleep. Furthermore, they had moments—and even extended periods of time throughout the day—in which they felt fatigued, listless, and in many cases outright exhausted. Most had some strategy for keeping alert during work hours, ranging from frequent trips to the coffeemaker to multiple doses of an energy drink. Some simply went home utterly drained of energy, and did what they could to make it through the evening until they hit the pillow, usually later than they knew they should.

This high incidence of fatigue, however, was not even the most alarming part. Jake learned that many of his colleagues took sleeping pills to actually get any sleep at all. This sent a shiver down his spine because the idea of self-medicating, even with something as mild as sleep aids, carried with it memories that Jake preferred to avoid. He suppressed that line of thought, and returned to the issue at hand: people needed assistance to get them to sleep, and then needed different assistance to help them wake up. That couldn't be right.

That morning's altercation with Kylee had surprised Jake. What had begun as a simple lizard-brain moment turned into a full-blown quest for truth. After a few conversations with colleagues and friends, Jake was back in front of his computer, hoping to find some science to back up what he intuitively knew to be true: being unrested and sleep-deprived opens the door to a very active lizard brain.

He found two articles particularly interesting. The first discussed a study where pairs of people had been studied over fourteen days on various levels of sleep. Not surprisingly, people who slept less fought more, and the less sleep they had, the more bitter their arguments, and the less they liked the other person in the study.[11] The second was a study where participants were given emotional intelligence, creative, and cooperative problem-solving tests after being kept awake for about two and a half days. The study found that sleep deprivation, perhaps unsurprisingly, had a significant negative impact on emotional intelligence in general, as well as on creative thinking and problem solving.[12] As he read, Jake could see all four lizard brain characteristics clearly reflected in the results.

Jake thought about whether or not he ever got enough sleep. He often felt tired, but that seemed so normal that it had never crossed his mind to question it. But stilling his lizard brain was the new quest, and if finding a way to get more rest was a part of achieving that, then he was committed to doing it. He began to wonder if getting good rest meant more than just sleeping longer hours. Were there ways to rest during the day? What activities caused him to feel even more tired, and what if there were ways to do them differently—or perhaps, not at all?

Suddenly Jake realized he wasn't really sure how to begin a better regimen for resting. Would he have to change routines at night? Did he need to sleep in later? That would be problematic, because he had spent years developing the self-discipline of getting up early to get to work. Was he going to have to choose between stilling his lizard brain, and changing his habits? Jake figured out that in order to still the lizard inside him, he would indeed need to get more rest. He wasn't totally convinced that this would actually work, but he did know that the opposite was perfectly clear—the lizard brain jumped to take over when he was tired. *Just ask Kylee*, he scoffed to himself.

However, Jake also realized that in order to get more rest, he would have to challenge the very characteristics of the lizard brain itself, which would require breaking habits, and building new routines. That sounded like a lot of hard work. And with a quick laugh, Jake felt he'd discovered why coffee was so important (and it certainly was to everyone he knew). The row after row of keep-you-awake energy drinks, and certainly all the sleeping pills, were so prevalent because sometimes it seemed like trying to bring about meaningful change was more exhausting than just remaining tired. Regardless, Jake was committing himself to more rest. He just needed to figure out what that would look like.

Strategy Two

ENJOY
Learning to Love Life Again

Finding new ways to get more rest was more challenging than Jake had anticipated. He let Laurie in on his newest discovery, and, to his surprise, she was enthusiastic. Laurie had suspected for some time that rest was important, and she welcomed the idea of going to bed earlier. But they both felt the truth of the saying, "Old habits die hard." Going to bed earlier just felt odd. "Uncomfortable" was probably more like it. There seemed to be a certain cachet to staying up late, and it took a few days to realize that by missing the late news and late shows, they weren't really missing all that much. Certainly nothing that couldn't be caught up on the next day.

Still, he felt as though this change was meaningful, and he was eager to find other ways to still the very lizard brain that had created the father who would publicly criticize his daughter before even saying good morning, and the husband who would fight so vociferously with his wife over an oil change.

The second discovery came at Jake in a much different way. He hadn't set out to have another discovery at all, really. He was simply paying attention to when he could feel himself falling into old patterns such as trying to win simple arguments, and to how he responded when he felt out of control. He wasn't sure

74

that getting more rest would cure all of this, but he suspected it would help. He had read too much about sleep deprivation (and frankly, experienced it too deeply himself) to ignore the facts. And then he discovered another potential tool in learning to manage his lizard brain.

Jake and Laurie had been invited to go with some friends who had four tickets to a minor-league baseball game. It had been a while since they had seen a game, and his girls had activities of their own for the evening, so it would just be the four adults. Jake realized it had been a long time since he had felt this much enthusiasm. He and Laurie did manage to go out every once in a while, but making plans with friends, and going to a baseball game, were not things that he did often anymore. He was a little surprised at how much he was looking forward to it.

When he and Laurie entered the stadium with their friends, he was overwhelmed by the sights and smells, and by how much it felt like he had come home. He felt like a kid again. With beers and hot dogs in hand, they all took their seats and watched as the players warmed up on the field. A feeling of peace came over Jake as he took it all in. He was engaged with everything—with the conversation, with the sight of the crowd, with the taste of his beer and hot dog, with the cacophony of sound preceding the opening pitch. Everything felt magnified, somehow.

The game began, and Jake was hardly aware of anything else at that moment. There were no worries about anything going on at work or at home. He had completely let go of the ups and downs of the past few weeks. No meltdowns, no lizards. He simply felt present. There was a quiet contentment—joy even—despite the spilled beer, and Laurie rolling her eyes as he loudly denounced the umpire's eyesight.

It wasn't until the seventh inning stretch that anything about the lizard brain entered his mind. But somewhere around hearing the crowd singing about peanuts and Crackerjacks, Jake had the random thought: *where's the lizard now?* He was so caught up in enjoyment that his lizard brain was virtually undetectable. He didn't want to disengage from the moment to explore why, but he made a mental note to return to the question later.

Back home after the game, as he and Laurie got ready for bed, Jake began again to consider when and why the lizard brain is active, and why and when it is still. As he slipped into deep thought, he abruptly remembered that getting a good night's rest was crucial to stilling the lizard, and that not letting his mind begin to wind down was not helpful. Rather than trying not to forget his current thoughts, he took out a piece of paper and wrote: *Lizard brain active when tired. Lizard brain still when having fun.* Secure in the knowledge that he could pick up his thoughts again tomorrow, he got into bed, and soon drifted off.

When Jake awoke the following morning, he realized he felt fully rested. It was a typical weekend morning—Laurie and the kids laid low until almost 10:00 a.m. With the house quiet, Jake sipped a cup of coffee and lazily read the paper: first world affairs and some financial stories, and then the sports section.

He thumbed through the various sporting events and outcomes, and he found himself lingering on the major league baseball statistics. As he was seeing who was winning each division, and studying each win-loss percentage, he remembered how he had felt at the game the night before. What was it about being in that ballpark that brought him so much peace? He thought about his note to himself from the night before, and he opened his laptop and proceeded to search for clues about whether being at a baseball game could have anything to do with stilling the lizard brain.

He wasn't actually sure, at first, what to look for. How could he distinguish the important factor in the evening's activity? Was it the energy from being in a crowd of people? A crowd certainly had energy, but it also brought frustration with lines for food and restrooms, and traffic snarls in parking lots—though Jake hadn't been too disturbed by those things last night. (His calmness had been yet another indication, he thought, of a still lizard.) Was it the sport itself? Jake knew that he always felt better when he was physically active but he hadn't been playing, so that wasn't it. Was it the rhythm of baseball? The stats? The competition? Or was he overthinking it all, and his quiet lizard brain was simply because the whole experience had been fun?

Jake sat in his chair, wanting to figure out whether or not having fun had anything to do with the lizard brain. And if it did, then how could someone have fun more? Surely that would still the lizard brain! This made him wish he could win the lottery, so that he could stop working, and just have fun. Realizing that he had fallen into an all-too-common trap of thinking in extremes, he still entertained himself for a few minutes imagining, "What if?" He knew that many people who came into unexpected money in this way ended up miserable and lonely. He laughed a little and wondered why so many people still daydreamed about such winnings—but hadn't he just done the same?

Regardless, the baseball game, and his reaction to it, was real. The lizard brain had been undetectable at the game. What's more, the effect of stilling the lizard had lingered. He had slept well, felt rested, and, even now, his lizard brain was tranquil.

It hit him that he didn't ever go to the ballpark anymore. He hadn't been to one in a long time. Jake was a little dumbfounded at the realization, because he simply couldn't fathom why he wouldn't go to games. His mind searched for the reasons: work, time, money, the girls, Laurie, etc. All of these excuses sounded good, and made sense. And then there were his past ties to the game. Perhaps he had avoided it out of fear that being there would be painful. And maybe it would have been painful long ago, but last night's game had been nothing but joyful. Perhaps it was time to reconsider all of his excuses for not going.

Jake began to think about other things that he enjoyed doing, and wondered why he didn't get to do them anymore, either. He liked to ride his bike. He loved to go fishing. He used to enjoy playing poker with his buddies on Friday nights. He really liked going out to dinner with the whole family, or having a date night with Laurie. And he realized it wasn't that he didn't *get* to do them, he simply didn't. *Insert previous list of excuses here*, he thought.

Jake decided to make a list of everything in life that he enjoyed. It was long. He then considered each item and asked himself why he didn't really do it any longer. It was a painful exercise for him, and he could feel his lizard brain heating up as he tried to answer honestly the question of why. Jake realized that life had brought him to a place where he no longer even thought about some of the things that he enjoyed so much. He knew that life wasn't just about having fun—but it wasn't just about working and accomplishing, either. He decided he needed to reacquaint himself with some of the things that used to bring him joy. He stopped shy of creating a document of all the enjoyable things he'd like to get back to. But he suspected that even just thinking about his "fun list," as he had started to call it, was going to help keep his lizard brain calm.

Laurie had come downstairs with Kylee and Katy. All three of them had dressed, and were heading out shopping together. Jake decided he would join them and take them to lunch at their favorite burger joint, grumbling all the while so they wouldn't suspect that he was actually enjoying himself.

Jake was pleased with the two strategies he had discovered so far. He had come to understand that he could better cope with his lizard brain when he felt rested. Furthermore, he knew his lizard brain got calm when he was enjoying things he loved, or even when he just thought about these things. And it wasn't just him who noticed. One evening Laurie, made a comment about how she'd noticed his demeanor had changed when they were at the baseball game. She said that he had been the best version of himself, and she thought it was because he was so caught up in the enjoyment of the evening. When she said this, he thought about how she herself got a sparkle in her eyes when she was teaching, or doing something else she enjoyed, and he loved seeing it. And Jake knew he had to bring back some fun back into their lives.

Strategy Three

WELLNESS
Inner and Outer Health

One of the things on Jake's fun list was going to his daughters' volleyball games. The summer club season was in full swing, and the girls played in a competitive league. One Friday night, Laurie had helped the girls pack their duffel bags, and as soon as Jake got home from work, they all went off to the gym where the girls had an important regional match. Even though Jake felt tired from the week at the office, he couldn't help but notice that his lizard brain was calm. He felt a sense of peace, and it was either his excitement to be watching his daughters compete, or the pleasure of spending time with his family, that stilled his lizard brain.

The match was intense. Both teams were playing well, and were tied with two wins each. During the last game, Jake and Laurie cheered from the stands, enjoying the rising tension over the final outcome as the opposing team served for what could be game point. Kylee was on the bench, but Katy was on the court and, as she jumped to spike the ball, the setter stumbled underneath her. Katy came down hard, with both girls caught up in a tangle of limbs, and Jake's heart went into his throat as he heard his daughter's shriek of pain.

Jake and Laurie flew out of the stands as coaches and teammates alike surrounded Katy where she lay writhing in pain.

After a lengthy huddle, and many ice packs to try to slow the swelling, Jake lifted his daughter off the court and headed to the emergency room.

The broken bone in Katy's ankle was obvious on the x-ray. Fortunately, it was a clean break, and the doctor thought it would heal well. In spite of that, Katy was going to be on crutches for a while. Volleyball was over for her for the summer. As for her school's season in the fall, the doctor would only say, "Let's wait and see."

Katy made it through the weekend with some small doses of pain meds, something Jake and Laurie were very careful to control. By Sunday night, it already seemed as though the family was getting used to Katy being on the mend. Jake and Laurie even hoped that Katy might enjoy the extra attention enough that she wouldn't mind her sister finishing out the season on the court without her.

Jake went to work on Monday morning thinking about his family. Not long after he got to work, he remembered the two ways to still his lizard brain—rest and fun. He realized how selfish it would be for him to think that *his* fun on Friday night had come to an abrupt end, and he began to wonder how Katy would handle her forced inactivity. Aside from volleyball, it seemed all his daughters wanted to do was sleep in or sunbathe, so how bad could it be?

At that moment, his phone rang. It was Laurie, calling to tell Jake about *his* daughter and the bad mood she was in. Laurie described how Katy seemed angry that morning, and how she and Katy had practically shouted at each other over how much milk Laurie put in Katy's oatmeal. *Oatmeal?* Jake was amazed, but then remembered his own overreaction to oil changes and T-shirts. "Sounds like her lizard brain is taking over," Jake said, and it struck him just how active the lizard brain can be when someone isn't well.

The instant he thought it, he knew it to be true. Until he had begun learning about the lizard brain, he never would have seen it this way, but he had always known that the better he felt physically, the better he could handle stresses in his life. Perhaps because he had been an athlete and knew what it was both to be fit and to struggle with an injury, but Jake had long ago made a commitment to fitness, and he could see how his regular workouts clearly impacted other areas of his life. Laurie was committed to fitness, too. She was passionate about yoga, encouraged the girls to be as active as possible, and made sure they all ate reasonably healthy meals. Jake saw plenty of colleagues and friends who struggled to maintain good health, but he had always done pretty well in this arena.

But he had never stopped to think about exactly how physical heath influenced one's overall well-being. And now he wondered. Would being healthy still the lizard brain? Did sick people, or people who had to live with chronic pain, just have to live with active lizard brains? Katy's injury, and her subsequent bad mood, caused him to think deeply about physical health. And this seemed like more of a catch-22 than his previous discoveries. One needed to be well to help still the lizard, but everything about how to get well—staying fit, eating a good diet, and dealing with pain—was difficult, and sure to wake the lizard.

This played out in living color in Jake's household over the next six weeks as Katy's crabbiness continued. Her pain had given way to frustration, which then morphed into impatience to just be done with the whole thing. There were a few more episodes similar to what Kylee had dubbed "the Oatmeal Incident," and Jake could see the lizard brain at work in each of them.

To try to distract Katy from both her limitations and her irritability, Jake asked for her help in researching the link between good health and stilling the lizard brain. He was already familiar with some of the science behind wellness and how it affected mood, but he also wanted Katy to be aware of it. He was thrilled to see that, on her own, she began to learn more about the lizard brain, and how it related to the wellness of the body.

Jake felt that he had officially discovered a third strategy for dealing with the lizard brain—good physical health. Physical health in general was a topic that was written about prolifically, both on the internet and in print. And while there were countless people writing about the benefits of good physical health, Jake's interest was specifically in how health—both good and bad—affected the brain. He found articles that explained the correlation between good physical health and great emotional health, between physical wellness and the ability to get good rest, between physical health and good relationships. And there were many more links.

Jake realized, once again, that getting well physically in order to still the lizard would be a direct challenge to the lizard brain's four characteristics, making lasting change especially difficult. *But*, he thought, *the benefits of accomplishing it would be amazing!*

So that's three strategies, he thought. And then he set out to find more.

Strategy Four

INVEST
To Give Oneself Away

The game of finding, recognizing, and (hopefully) stilling the lizard started to become commonplace for Jake. Whether driving to work or sitting in the quiet of his home, he was developing a constant awareness of how the lizard brain played itself out in his life. Not surprisingly, Jake found it easier to see the lizard running amok in others than in himself. He readily identified the lizard brain in the people he worked with, and with his daughters and his wife. He certainly saw it through the windshield of his car, and in just about every public place he went. But Jake was wise enough to know that he needed to understand his own lizard brain before he could help others with theirs.

It was a typical Wednesday at work when Jake got a call from his wife, who let him know that they were going to be busy on Saturday. This wasn't welcome news for Jake, as he had planned to spend the weekend getting a few projects done at home. And, okay—also to watch the game on TV. Laurie went on to say that she had signed them both up to be officials at a local youth Special Olympics event being held downtown.

Jake felt his lizard brain begin to stir, but managed to catch himself. Laurie rarely asked for anything, and he knew this was the kind of thing that would mean a lot to her. So instead of protesting against the plan and making excuses for getting out of it, he simply said, "Great. Should be fun."

As he hung up the phone, he sat back and tried to make sense of what he was feeling. Guilt for sure, because it didn't really sound like fun to him at all, and a big part of him was hoping something would come up to get him out of it. And he definitely felt frustration—frustration over having to give up his plans for someone else's. Not only was he going to be missing something he had been looking forward to—watching the game—but he was also going to be engaging in something that felt a little awkward to him—the Special Olympics. Well, maybe a lot awkward.

From there he started to think about all of the reasons he was right to feel so frustrated. Wasn't it right to be upset over having his weekend decided for him without any discussion? Wasn't it right that he do some chores around the house? Wasn't it right that he should get to relax a little after a full week of work and evenings spent focused on the girls and their activities? As he sat and stewed, he kept returning to his frustration over having no control over his own weekend, and that thought was followed by a sudden realization. *Control! Being Right!* This was a new layer to his frustration. After all of his learning about the lizard brain, to still be so blind-sided by its tendencies. And then on top of that, to know where his frustrations were coming from, and yet to still feel them so strongly!

Jake mentally threw his hands up in surrender. He somehow pushed all thoughts of the phone call and the coming weekend aside and went back to work.

Saturday morning came with bright sunshine and warm temperatures, so it was clear that the event was going to go forward as planned. Jake had resigned himself to just getting through the day, and while he took some comfort in seeing Laurie's pleasure and excitement, his own enthusiasm was a little lacking. They arrived at the stadium, checked in at the organizing tent, and were assigned the job of being timers on the racetrack. Each was given a stopwatch, but Jake would soon learn the watches were more of a formality than a necessity.

On some level, Jake was still stewing about his lost weekend. But as the athletes began to gather at the track, he became distracted by all the activity, and his mood began to change. Still unsure about exactly what to do as timer for the 100-yard dash, Jake nonetheless was aware of the excitement that was building as the kids prepared for the race.

And then the race began. The spectators cheered, and Jake saw smiles of pure joy on the faces of several runners. Some of the kids ran with focus and determination, while others seemed to be okay just being on the track. Jake quickly realized that his stopwatch wasn't going to be crucial. While he still timed the athletes, Jake got completely caught up in the enjoyment of seeing kids having so much fun. And the families and friends, as well—everyone poured onto the track to congratulate their athletes at the end of each race, irrespective of how they'd done.

As other heats started and ended, Jake found himself completely absorbed in the day's events. He took part in several post-race celebrations, and at one point was the lead cheerleader for a young girl who barely made it down the track. It was exhilarating.

After the races, Jake and Laurie helped measure the shot put and the long jump, and much like in the first race, there was a blend of both athletes who were serious about the competition, and those who were happy just to be participating.

By about 1:00 the event was coming to a close, and after helping with some cleanup and saying good-bye to some of the athletes and their families, Jake and Laurie headed toward the car. Jake was both exhausted, and completely relaxed. Seeing his expression, it seemed it was all Laurie could do to not say, "I told you so." Jake was quiet for much of the car ride home, as he was lost in his thoughts about the day. Finally, he told Laurie that he was grateful that she had signed him up to participate in the event with her. Together, they basked in the feeling of having done something meaningful, and Jake even asked about getting involved in more events.

At home, Jake grabbed a bottle of iced tea and went to sit in the backyard. He wondered why he was feeling such deep joy after the morning's event. Was it the kids? The families? Was it doing something challenging? Or did Jake simply feel peace around the fact that he had sacrificed some of his time for this important cause? He had given something of his that he valued, and it had helped bring joy to a large group of people.

Then it hit him. He wondered if the lizard was stilled when he was giving something of himself. Giving his time and his energy, perhaps? Certainly there was nobility and honor in giving, but could it be that it also had an effect on the lizard brain?

Jake got up from his chair, and went inside to his computer to see if he could find any information on how the brain responded to giving. To his amazement, he found a few really good articles on the topic. One showed brain scans of people who were put through a virtual reality simulation of escaping from a burning building. At some point they were asked to choose between stopping to help another person, or continuing with their own escape. Researchers were able to see activity in different areas of the brain based on whether they chose to help the other person or not. So clearly, altruistic behavior did have a big effect on the mind, and Jake felt comfortable deciding that giving to others was yet another way to still the lizard brain.

That night, he and Laurie went out to dinner. He had been sharing discoveries from his research with her all along, but now, finally, he told her all about that crazy day in the seminar, and what had triggered his journey. Laurie listened intently as Jake explained what he had come to understand about this part of the brain.

The evening was remarkable, as Laurie said she more fully understood what he'd been grappling with. She was particularly thrilled with his discovery that giving was a crucial component to stilling the lizard, and began to think of other ways for them to participate in more events like the Special Olympics. As they drove home, Jake ran through the mental list of strategies he now knew to still the lizard. Getting good rest, finding time to enjoy life, maintaining good physical health—and now, investing in others. These were four strategies that he was sure would help him manage his unruly lizard brain.

He didn't know it, but the discovery of one of the most obvious—and possibly most potent—strategies was still ahead of him. But as Jake fell asleep that night, he felt a deep gratitude for all that he had learned so far.

Strategy Five

RELEASE
Learning What It Means to Let Go

With his life comprised of family outings, late summer barbecues with friends, and productive work, Jake was content. The lizard seminar meltdown felt like a distant memory. His lizard brain still flared up now and then, but he was becoming increasingly skilled at catching it early, and seeing it for what it was. He was teaching himself to adopt new ways of thinking, and while familiarity was hard to let go of, being right was the most difficult dynamic to part with.

Jake actively worked on the four strategies he had discovered for keeping his lizard brain stilled. He was very aware of how much sleep he was getting, and looked for new ways to feel even more rested.

He was making more of an effort to go out with Laurie, catch some baseball games, and take every opportunity to be with his daughters. He grew increasingly aware of just how still his lizard brain actually was in his moments of enjoyment, and this was a great incentive to keep his new lifestyle going.

Laurie had invited him to do a yoga class with her a couple times a week, and though the competitive athlete in him wanted to hate it, he actually enjoyed it. Through the yoga classes, Jake's flexibility started to return, and this enabled him to be even more active, which he knew to be important to his overall well-being.

And Jake and Laurie signed up for an additional Special Olympics event taking place later that fall, and Jake was looking into how to get involved with the local organization in other ways as well.

It seemed eons ago that Jake had sat in the lizard seminar and experienced the breakdown that had launched his journey, and he thought about how far he had come since then. He felt freer than he had in years. Identifying when the lizard brain was overactive had become a part of who he was. But it didn't seem to matter how adept he became at recognizing, and even stilling, his lizard brain—it continued to make its presence known in various ways.

Though Jake's effort to still his lizard brain had been largely internal, it was now beginning to have an outward effect—a change that was noticed by both Laurie and the girls. There were episodes in the car, the kitchen, around the TV remote, and certainly with the girls' apparel choices that used to trigger overreactions from Jake. Laurie was the first to notice the positive changes in his behavior, and she'd mentioned it to him a few times.

Jake was comfortable telling his family what he'd learned about the lizard brain, but his own lizard brain still felt too out of control yet to share what he was learning with anyone else. In particular, he could not seem to shake the need to always be right. Jake recognized that this need plagued him in a big way. This part of his lizard brain had run wild for so long, it sometimes felt impossible to catch. He was getting better at seeing it in hindsight, but catching it as it was happening with his daughters, Laurie, or someone at work seemed almost impossible. Furthermore, he realized that the need to be right was strongest in him with the people he loved the most. He had made a mental note to find out why that was.

One Friday morning, as Jake was getting ready to leave for work, Laurie told him that some friends of theirs were going though hard times, and Jake's outrage grew the more she told him. The husband of a married couple they knew had admitted that he was addicted to the prescription drug Oxycontin.

Too angry to listen to her tell the story behind the addiction, Jake found himself incensed at the idea that a father of three children would allow himself to get dependent on drugs. Multiple times, as Laurie tried to tell the story, Jake would cut her off and say that the guy was stupid, thoughtless, and selfish.

Laurie seemed increasingly upset the longer he talked. Jake's lizard brain at this point was so loud that he misunderstood her reaction entirely. Jake assumed that she was joining him in condemning their friend's bad behavior, but as his tirade went on and on, it began to occur to him that Laurie was instead dismayed over the harshness of his response.

Here, front and center, was the Jake of old, with his crazy lizard brain on full display. Jake would later learn that an overactive lizard brain completely disarms one's ability to recognize the lizard at all. So when he left for work, he took the out-of-control lizard with him. All the way to the office, Jake replayed the conversation in his head, affirming the rightness of his position (a favorite trick of the lizard brain). It seemed as though time alone only bolstered his certainty around his moral position.

When he got home that evening, Laurie cautiously asked why he'd had such an extreme reaction. Her question nearly sparked another outburst, but just in time Jake remembered the new journey he was on, and was able not only to moderate his defensiveness over Laurie's question, but also to take a second, more objective look at his reaction that morning.

He was caught somewhere between embarrassment and curiosity. He felt some shame over lashing out, but also found himself asking why there was something about this scenario that had triggered such a strong reaction in him. He quickly saw that finding fault in someone else was essential to believing they were wrong. Then by default, Jake thought, he was right. *Ugh! There it is again!* His need to be right. He tried to consider both the story and his thoughts about it, but he always found himself returning to the anger.

It wasn't until Saturday afternoon that Jake finally had a breakthrough (perhaps better described as a personal "break-in," because of the emotions attached to it). It came when Jake finally saw the connection between the friend with the addiction issue and his own story. Jake's addiction all those years before was so shameful to him that he had tried to bury it in the past, where he would never have to think about it again. Perhaps, Jake thought, his reaction to his friend's predicament was so strong precisely because it had so deeply touched a nerve with regard to his own un-talked-about, un-dealt-with, and certainly unforgiven past.

Even after he had made this connection between his friend's struggles and his own, he tried to push this unhappy part of his past back into the dark, but it was too late. It had come fully into the light, and had to be dealt with.

There had been challenges in learning about the lizard brain, but none as painful as having to deal with his own past. Jake began to realize that his inability to control the "must-be-right" part of the lizard brain was directly linked to this unresolved issue. It was so simple for Jake to find fault in so many people. Maybe being right was the easiest way to shield himself from his own feelings of guilt and shame.

Jake thought about discussing this with Laurie, but didn't have the courage to do so. He believed they had an unwritten and (in his mind) serious pact to never speak of his past addiction again. But eventually, he mustered up the guts to speak with Laurie, and it was both terrifying and cleansing. They hadn't once talked about Jake's addiction since he had beaten it, and he broke down as he told Laurie about how terrifying it had been to slip into such a dark place. Together they were able to see how this part of his life had festered beneath the surface, and how it colored how he now viewed others. Jake carried shame with him every day, and was finally beginning to realize what a heavy burden it was. And now, for the first time in their eighteen-year marriage, Jake and Laurie were able to speak about this issue that was once so taboo.

Though they had talked about his research before, Jake brought Laurie up to date on where he was in his pursuit to "still the lizard." There was a knot in his stomach as he admitted how the must-be-right factor was still so dominant. And Laurie echoed his earlier realization, pointing out that his need to be right all the time had to be linked to his inability to forgive himself for his past. It was not a particularly comfortable thought. But as he sat with it, he realized that it was indeed difficult to offer other people mercy when he couldn't even offer it to himself.

If he could learn to release himself from his past errors, he said, then he would likely be better at offering this same grace to others. But Laurie wisely pointed out that offering grace, mercy, and acceptance to others first might be the best way to still the must-be-right trait in himself.

As the conversation came to a close, he felt exhausted. Jake and Laurie both would later remember this as being one of the most meaningful and healing conversations of their marriage.

Releasing himself, and learning to release others, was going to take some time and practice. Jake expected that it wouldn't be easy, given that the scars were old, and ran deep. But the connection between a lack of forgiveness, a clinging to past mistakes, and an agitated lizard brain was unmistakable. And so Jake concluded that releasing people (himself included) could be the fifth strategy to learning to still his lizard brain.

Strategy Six

EXECUTE
The Difference Between Knowing and Doing

Jake's personal mission had officially shifted, and he became more and more open to the possibility of sustainable change. It was only a few months ago that he was getting up every day, pursuing excellence and success in the only way he knew—in the external world. It was jarring to consider just how different he felt over the past few months, taking a journey into this new internal world. He felt a new level of clarity, but also discomfort, as if something were still missing.

He thought again about each of the strategies he had learned.

He had found out why resting and getting better sleep was so important, and how this had really come into play in his own world. He'd learned so much about how being rested helped him think differently, and how his lizard brain was stilled when he got good sleep.

He now knew that taking the time to enjoy life with his family and friends was much more than just a feel-good strategy. It was something far more important, and had a much more lasting impact, than he had ever before suspected.

Jake then considered what it meant to be physically healthy. It was still often easier for him to see the lizard brain at work in others, and it was unsurprising when he saw an overactive lizard brain in coworkers and friends who chose not to make their physical health a priority. In addition to being so important in and of itself, he had realized that the better his health, the better he rested as well. *Two strategies for one*, Jake thought.

And then there was the idea of investing. Not only had Jake begun to recognize investing in others as a strategy to still his own lizard brain, but over time he had also come to realize that he loved working with the Special Olympics and seeing the impact the events and activities had on the participants and their families.

The strategy of release may have been the most powerful of them all. Letting go of things that once hurt so badly, and learning to forgive himself—and then, subsequently, others—may have had the single greatest effect on him during his entire journey. Jake now understood how learning to let go of the pain from the past was a freedom that he hadn't even known was possible—partly because he had never recognized the prison he had put himself in by holding on to that pain. He knew there was so much more work to do, but just embarking on the journey had already had a deep impact on how he viewed life.

Jake thought that he had unlocked some secrets to living a fuller, more meaningful life, and yet his life still felt incomplete. Oddly, he was restless in a way he couldn't define. And then it struck him.

He remembered that he had once heard someone say there is a difference between knowledge and wisdom. He couldn't remember where he'd heard it, but the gist of it was this: the difference between knowledge and wisdom is in how one actually lives.

Perhaps his restlessness came from the fact that knowing all of these strategies, even knowing about the lizard brain itself, was useless unless he acted on that knowledge. And he realized that, for some reason, the idea of acting on it scared him, though he wasn't sure why. Why would he feel fear about acting on these strategies that were so life-giving, so right, and so good? Heck, Jake thought, he had already begun to sleep better, and to receive the benefits of such rest. Why would he feel trepidation about going to more baseball games, or hanging out with the girls? About working out at the gym, and engaging with Special Olympics? About feeling what it means to truly forgive? It was all so good—and yet there was something almost terrifying in it.

It was taking the giant leap from knowledge to wisdom, Jake realized. He had acquired plenty of knowledge, he knew. But all that knowledge with no application had no value. The problem was that applying it took energy, commitment, and a willingness to change.

Then it hit him like a ton of bricks. Stilling the lizard brain was about embracing the effort needed to change. If people set out to learn about themselves, they can do so quite easily, and still never really make any changes at all. In fact, Jake thought, this was the very reason he had the meltdown to begin with. All that knowledge, but little to no actual change. Jake knew in that moment that if he didn't begin executing the strategies of stilling the lizard brain, he would end up right back where he started. He had begun to do some of the work already, he realized, but his focus had still been on what he knew about each of the strategies. He would now need to shift his focus and his efforts to what he could do about them.

Executing the strategies meant catching himself when he was trying to be right with Laurie and the girls. Executing meant going to baseball games with Laurie, or getting out on weekends with his daughters. Executing meant giving some of his time to the Special Olympics. Executing most certainly meant getting better sleep at night, and also rest during the day. Finally, executing meant learning how to let go of past pain, as well as the need to be perfect. And while all of this seemed so good and so right, Jake knew that executing meant leaving the life he knew. That was a frightening thought.

Jake understood "the devil we know" meant that most people would even choose evil over change. *It is precisely the devil we know that allows us to accumulate all kinds of knowledge, and still remain stuck*, he thought.

For a few days, Jake tried to think of ways to make more doable the changes he knew he needed to make. Finally, he realized that there was simply no way. If it were easy, then everyone would have stilled lizard brains. The trick, if there was one, was simply to embrace the discomfort and move through it, rather than trying so hard to avoid it.

This, then, was the final piece of the puzzle—to execute on the other five strategies. And execution meant change. Permanent change. Scary though that seemed, Jake felt sure that this was the very journey he was meant to be on. The fear began to fade, and was finally replaced by a sense of excitement.

NOT SO FICTION

REALITY IS MERELY AN ILLUSION,
ALBEIT A VERY PERSISTENT ONE.

– Albert Einstein

Jake is real. Well, kind of. Though I originally set out to write a fictional story, what emerged was as much autobiography as it was fiction.

After proofreading the chapter on being right, my wife approached me and gently asked if I'd read this part of the book. Seeing my incredulous expression, she said, "I know you wrote it, but have you *read* it?" What she semi-jokingly was pointing out was that, though I personally spent time researching and developing a deep understanding of the lizard brain, I was in no way immune to its effects. Yes, my lizard brain, like yours, can be a real nuisance. And that's putting it mildly!

It was at that point that I realized that I was penning an autobiography as much as I was trying to impart truth through the telling of Jake's story.

From the very beginning, I wanted you, the reader, to be drawn in by Jake's odyssey to the point that you would find yourself living it, in real life. Because we each have a lizard brain, myself included. I suppose that, had Jake stayed in that fateful seminar, I could have written more of a non-fiction book about what the lizard brain really is. Perhaps he could have learned about it from a great teacher in a classroom. Many of us want to learn that way.

But I can think of at least two problems with writing a non-fiction book about the lizard brain. First, it might be boring. Learning about neuroanatomy, and how we think and respond to things as human beings—it just doesn't sound like as much fun as reading a story. Secondly, I think this is the type of curriculum that begs for a pragmatic, real-life understanding rather than a scientific perspective. Don't get me wrong—I am grateful for all of the neuroscientists who have dedicated their lives to uncovering what we now understand about the human brain. I felt it was important to add these elements of research to the story so that you could know that, while Jake's life has been fabricated, the research he finds throughout his journey has not.

So we wrote the story. I say "we" because truly this took a village. Perhaps there are some super humans who can sit down and create a story that is consistent, sequential, and interesting, but I am not one of them. Jake would be a hollow character with virtually no storyline if I alone had created him.

But I digress. I want to get back to the person I always hoped this story would be about: you! Yes, I understand that Jake is a middle-aged, male American with two kids and a loving (and patient) wife. I realize that not everyone is a financial advisor, nor does everyone have the passion for self-improvement that Jake has. But we each have a lizard brain. Every one of us.

Therefore it is my hope that as you read about his story, Jake's breakdowns, his breakthroughs, and everything in between, you will discover something meaningful about yourself.

Perhaps you have been frustrated by a lack of authentic growth in your life. Maybe you have recognized your inability (or unwillingness) to bring about change. You may not have freaked out about it publicly, but the frustration was there.

So let's take a quick review of the four lizard brain characteristics, and try to uncover which of these affects you the most in this season of your life. Since everyone has a lizard brain, you should be able to identify at least one or two of these characteristics at play. Quite honestly, we all have all four characteristics, but at first it may be important for us to focus on how just one or two are affecting our ability to grow, to be better people, to be better wives, husbands, children or friends, to earn more money, or to otherwise change in any positive and lasting way.

FAMILIARITY

So, how 'bout it? Are you influenced by the characteristic of familiarity? Do you find yourself repeating patterns endlessly? Does the idea of taking a different way to work, sitting in a different place at church, or drinking a different brand of beer bother you? Have you ever noticed how changes in your work environment affect you? Are new incentives or programs at work difficult to embrace? Often in our workshops I ask people to do something simple, like crossing their arms differently, or clasping their hands by shifting their fingers over one space. Something so minor bothers most people, and some truly hate doing it. The point of the exercise is, of course, to demonstrate just how powerful this particular characteristic of our lizard brain is.

The lizard in each of us loves familiar patterns. We feel safe in our patterned lives, and our lizard brain loves safety! And, truth be told, many of our patterns and familiar ways are not bad for us. But they may become bad when we cannot navigate change. How many times have we worked for a company who has just gone through a software conversion? How much pain and frustration was caused by the lizard brain's inability to accept the new system simply because it was different from what we were used to, even when it was better? How often are we irked by something only because it is unfamiliar?

If this describes you, don't worry. You are one of countless people who follows patterns, and longs for what is familiar. But it is likely that the very patterns you cling to could be holding you back from making some substantial changes in your life. For each of the characteristics of the lizard brain, there are antidotes—things you can do to still that part of your inner lizard. With familiarity, I recommend going out of your way to try to break some simple patterns. Take a different road when driving to work. Walk on a different path, watch a different show, try a different flavor of ice cream. Make a conscious choice to do something that is unfamiliar to you. When you manage this, know that you are developing a skill. And do it with small things first. We often want to begin by tackling the big things, but then we get frustrated because we have not first practiced with the little things. Break familiar patterns in small ways. Be open to doing things differently, however uncomfortable it may feel.

BEING RIGHT

Perhaps you are someone who must always be in the right. This part of the lizard brain is deeply entrenched in many people, but it largely goes unnoticed, because in order to identify your own need to be right, you have to question it. Can you see that even questioning yourself about your own desire to be right agitates the lizard brain? If this characteristic affects you, (and often we have to hear this from others around us) I would ask you to try to be aware of it as it is happening. Yes, we most often see it after the fact, but what if you could catch yourself in the moment of wanting to be right? This lizard-brain characteristic, in particular, is so insidious because we can feel threatened if we feel we are in danger of being wrong. We often have only one question in our minds: am I am right, or am I wrong?

I propose that we need alternate questions that we can ask ourselves. Questions such as, "Do I want to be right, or do I want to have peace?" or, "Do I want to be right, or do I want a good relationship?" This is certainly not to imply that there is never a time to be right, because there is. In a moral situation, or in a legal situation, we may well need to be right, and to take a stand. But insisting on being right about a topic or situation is very often unnecessary. (Though it isn't to our lizard brains.)

And this is what I mean by learning to "still the lizard." When we are able to be in a moment, realize our deep desire to be right, and then choose to not fight for the win, we have effectively calmed our lizard brain. Try it. You will be amazed at the freedom you experience by not engaging in the battle to be right.

HABITS

The next characteristic Jake had to discover was habits. For the record, the lizard brain doesn't perceive habits as being good or bad. In fact, it loves habits so much that it considers all habits to be good. But, if we are being honest with ourselves, we know perfectly well that we have some bad habits. In our story, Jake had a "bad" habit of constantly checking his e-mail. I could have made him a smoker, or someone who bites his fingernails, or given him some other bad habit. But instead I gave him a mindless compulsion to check e-mail. It is a common enough habit in our wired world that many of us have it.

The lizard brain simply loves habits. Good ones, bad ones—it doesn't really matter. Habits of any kind help us to survive, because they allow us to conserve energy. Once something has been done over and over again, the brain can go on autopilot, and no longer needs to expend energy considering what action to take. And if you think about it, this is a brilliant design.

For the record, most of us have plenty of good habits, but we rarely focus on those when we talk about compulsive, mindless behavior. Pick up a book on habits (and there are a ton of them), and you will find that they are almost always about breaking *bad* habits. There are very few books about good habits; the book-buying public wants to learn how to change the bad ones. And not only do we want to know how to break bad habits, we want to know how to do it quickly.

In fact, "breaking" a habit is not really how it works. I'm not convinced that one can ever truly break a habit. Instead, breaking a habit might be more correctly stated as starting a new one. To oversimplify the science, habits are actually the neural pathways that we have etched into our brains. Once established, those pathways will always be there. What you can do is replace a habit with something else—a new neural pathway—and weaken the first through disuse. And when talking about how long it takes to "break" a habit, scientists are referring to the length of time it takes for neurons to regenerate, and establish a new connection.

But it doesn't really matter how long it takes. What matters is how long you are willing to take with it. Perhaps the next story I write will be on habit *re*formation, and we can take a deeper look at the science then. In the meantime, if you want to form a new habit in your life and successfully supplant an old, bad one, it is important to know that you must first journey through three or four days of hell. That's right—hell. It was Winston Churchill who said, "If you're going through hell, keep going." The new habit will not feel comfortable at all. And leaving the bad one behind will most certainly feel awful. If you can get through the first three to four days, then you have a real shot at going the distance.

Unfortunately, our culture doesn't allow for suffering at any level. We don't embrace difficulty as part of the human experience, and in fact are bombarded by messages trying to teach us how not to have to go through challenges of any kind. This is in opposition to how the brain is designed to learn new skills, but it is the prevalent mindset in our get-everything-you-want, instant-gratification world. We want it easy, and we want it now.

In what ways could your life, or your business, be improved if you were able to start a new habit? My hope is that you are encouraged both by Jake's story, and by this quick reality-check on habit breaking and making.

CONTROL

Finally, we have control. Our lizard brain loves to be in control. But even more than it loves being *in* control, the lizard brain really hates the feeling of *losing* control. This characteristic is interesting in that it is best seen in the negative. When life feels in control, then the lizard brain is quiet and still. It is when we begin to feel like we are losing control that our inner reptile goes berserk, and it will want to reestablish control any way it can.

I suspect that this characteristic is possibly the most pervasive, and maybe even the most damaging, of them all. Worry, concern, anxiety, and fear (all emotions consistent with an active lizard brain) are usually focused on some future outcome. We think forward, and predict a negative result. What's interesting is that we don't know for certain that the outcome will be negative, and often we even have to admit that it probably won't be. This is where the lizard brain comes into play.

It's likely not the end result at all that is driving our anxiety, but rather our inability to control the outcome. When the lizard brain realizes that it can't control an outcome, it gets frantic, and we lose our ability to think rationally.

One key question I have been asking lately in workshops I do for clients has to do with anxiety. Most recently, I asked a group of about eighty managers and leaders to raise their hands if they felt as though their life was more anxious than they would like. Almost 100% of them raised their hands, and as we went deeper into a discussion of the lizard brain and control, it was apparent that much of their anxiety stemmed from their inability to control the future.

I suspect that this widespread anxiety is a silent epidemic in our culture. Perhaps it is so very pervasive because our inner desire to keep things in our control is often challenged by our deeper understanding of how much is actually outside of it. When I offer strategies to still this particular part of the lizard brain, I'm not trying to help people to get back into control. Rather, I want to help people still their lizard by helping them learn to experience peace when they feel out of control.

This is a great time for reflection. By now, you have a fundamental knowledge of what I mean by the lizard brain. You have read Jake's story, and have seen how each of the four characteristics impacted his life: familiarity, being right, habits, and control. Now, carefully consider which of these four attributes impacts you the most. Know that, to some degree, each one of them affects you. But it could be very meaningful for you to discover which is loudest in you.

*

Learning about the lizard brain is funny, because once you learn the traits you will see them everywhere you look in other people. But it is much more challenging to see the lizard brain at work in ourselves. And the purpose of this book is not to teach you how to judge others, but rather to have the courage to look inward, and see how your lizard brain is impacting your own life.

To help you accomplish this, I would like to give you a gift for having purchased the book, and taken the time to read Jake's story. My colleagues and I have designed and created the very first (we believe) Lizard Brain Assessment. It will only take a few minutes to complete, and you will get your results immediately.

Simply go to **www.lizardquiz.com** to take the assessment.

Your results page provides information about your score, and what the score means. Identifying where your lizard brain is too active could be one of the most important revelations you can have for improving your life.

How about it? Which of the four characteristics is affecting you the most? To become aware of this may be painful, but it will also be the necessary beginning of the journey to still your own lizard brain.

THE SIX STRATEGIES TO STILL YOUR LIZARD BRAIN

I have considered countless ways to still the lizard brain as I have been studying it, and teaching about it, for quite a few years. Though many scientists refer to a part of our brain as the lizard brain, or sometimes the reptilian brain, what I find very interesting about it is that if you brought twenty scientists together and asked each of them what they thought the lizard brain was, you might get twenty different answers. There is no consensus on what the lizard brain is. For some, it's a part of our physiology that sits at the base of the brain. For others, it is synonymous with the amygdala in our limbic system, though there is some consensus between those two groups that the lizard brain regulates our survival with regard to the fight or flight response. Still others think of the lizard brain as more of a concept—that while the brain as a whole has a functionality well beyond mere survival and physical responses, there is an instinctive part of the brain—the lizard brain—whose purpose is to guide those physical responses

119

to promote our survival. You can see how these two views of the lizard brain are similar. But whether it is an actual, physical section of the brain regulating fight or flight, or a metaphorical construct to help us understand our instinctual responses to perceived threats, the lizard brain is in each of us.

In taking what neuroscience has been discovering about the lizard brain, and trying to help people understand their visceral responses to things, I pieced together the four characteristics Jake discovered: familiarity, being right, habits, and control. By giving the lizard brain a well-defined framework, I have been able to help a lot of people.

But as I started to share this framework throughout the country, it didn't immediately occur to me that I hadn't created any solutions for it. I didn't have any strategies that I could offer for what to do with this framework once a person has learned it. So initially, though I was very excited about learning about the lizard brain, and I was certainly excited about sharing it with other people, it lacked any meaningful answer to the question, "Now what?" That is to say—what do we do with the information once we have it?

I was nearing the end of a workshop a few years ago, after teaching about the lizard brain for a while, when I realized that I hadn't defined any solutions for managing the lizard brain; I was only pointing out what it was. A participant raised his hand and said, "Well, I know we're coming to an end, but you're surely going to offer us strategy?" And, like Jake, I had a dark moment—suddenly discovering, in a room full of people waiting for an answer, that I was missing a crucial piece of the puzzle. At that point, I set out with my team to really brainstorm and research in order to create some tangible techniques to answer the question, "Now what?"

I still believe that there's great merit in pointing out the issue at hand, namely that we all have a loud lizard brain from time to time. I think there's value in understanding, at an academic level, what the lizard brain is, because we must know exactly what it is before we can know what to do with it.

But simply knowing about the lizard brain and how it drives us, while helpful, is not enough to enable us to actually do anything about it. So in the end, I defined what Jake discovered as the six different strategies to still his lizard brain. This is not a definitive list, and you may think of others that I haven't talked about here. But these are the six tactics I have chosen to help you to manage your lizard brain, instead of letting it always manage you.

REST

These strategies, by the way, are only in this particular order because the first letter of each word forms the word "rewire," which is the name of the organization that I founded. Many times, strategies are laid out in steps, implying an order of importance. But our strategies are neither sequentially import-ant, nor ordered according to any relative value. As you read about them, you may realize that four of the six are already things in your life that you're doing well, and that you only need to work on two of them. I haven't met many people who need to focus on all six. And the strategies are independent in the sense that as you read them, you can pick and choose what would best help you.

The first strategy Jake discovered was rest. A lack of sleep allows the lizard brain to thrive. If you have a habit that you don't like, isn't it usually much harder to resist it when you're tired? When you're tired, your defenses are down, and your high-er-level thinking is inhibited. So, if you'd like to create a new habit (or stop an existing one), you might want to think about how you can get more rest. The body of work that we now have for rest is too extensive to cover in this book. But even the most cursory of searches on Google about resting will produce abun-dant material to read. And we are discovering that rest means so much more than just getting good sleep. Recent research about learning to quiet your mind through a mindfulness practice is reinforcing what practitioners of meditation have known for centuries. And who hasn't experienced the restorative powers of an hour in a lawn chair, with a good book?

When I talk about rest and sleep in the workshops I do around the country, what I hear is that sleep deprivation is an epidemic in this country. We don't live in a well-rested nation because we don't value good sleep. Getting by on little sleep seems, rather, to be a badge of honor. It's what productive people do, right? Furthermore, we're a caffeine culture. We have Starbucks on every corner. Energy drinks have their own aisle in most grocery stores. And in high schools, Coke and Red Bull abound. Why do we need so much extra energy?

On the other side of the equation is sleep medication, either over-the-counter or prescription. The most-recent data from the National Center for Health Statistics tells us that approximately 12.8 million adults take a prescription sleep aid.[13] Exactly how many people, and which kind of medication, depends on the study. And then we need caffeine to get us get through the next day, forming a wicked cycle.

It's easy to say, "Just get more sleep," and hard to actually do. But what we know about the importance of the various stages of our sleep cycles is growing. We are learning more about how the stress hormone cortisol is flushed from the brain during deep sleep, for example. And we also now know that a lack of enough sleep is related to everything from weight gain to heart disease.[14] If a lack of sleep stresses so many biological systems, is it any wonder that our lizard brains are loud because of it?

The attendees in our workshops ask, "So, how much sleep should I get?" And for most adults, the recommended time is seven to eight hours. But quantity seems to matter less than quality. If you have ever woken from a full night's sleep still feeling exhausted, you know just what I mean. So what blocks the quality of your sleep? We know that alcohol, late at night, diminishes it by shifting our sleep cycles, and reducing REM sleep.[15] We also know that the screens on electronic devices have a blue wave of light that keeps our brains awake.[16] And have I mentioned caffeine?

If you are considering ways to improve the quality of your sleep, you may want to limit your alcohol and caffeine consumption prior to bedtime, and to not have any screen time after seven o'clock at night. Many screens on our cell phones and computers are now programmable to kill the blue wave of light by a certain time of day. Or you can purchase blue-blocker glasses if you really must watch screens at night.

How many of you became anxious reading that last paragraph? This points to another difficulty with changing our patterns around sleep. If someone tells us, "Hey, get better sleep!" and then shows us all the science to justify it, we won't disagree. But we all have habits we love, like late-night shows we want to watch. That's what can make stilling our lizard brains such a challenge. In order to still the lizard brain, we have to go against its desire for familiarity, habits, being right, and control. But the potential dividends are huge.

So rest is the first strategy in learning how to still your lizard brain. As Jake came to understand in the story, his lizard brain was active when he was unrested, and that affected how he acted during conflicts with his family. It made him realize that he needed to rest more. I would encourage you to consider the same practice. If you like to underline things in books, underline this: GET BETTER SLEEP!

ENJOY

At this point, I want to remind you that Jake had learned that you can't kill the lizard brain—you can only still it. And even if you were able to kill it, you wouldn't survive very long. Your lizard brain serves an important function—it keeps you alive.

The second strategy in trying to still the lizard brain is learning to enjoy life. Jake realized that his lizard brain was still when he was at a baseball game. I wrote the story such that, like many people, Jake worked hard, and spent a lot of hours at the office. And his personal life was what life becomes for a lot of people; after they have children, or just get to a certain stage of their life, it can feel like there's no longer room to do things just for the fun of it. People often tell us that they used to love to hunt, fish, knit, or whatever it might be, but for whatever reason, they just don't do it anymore. We have found that the older we get, the more we have to be intentional about doing the things we really enjoy.

I realize that you can't make your whole life nothing but one long pleasure. People ask, "Am I supposed to just have fun all the time, then?" No. That becomes black-and-white thinking. We go from "I can't do it ever, any of the time" to "I can do that all the time," and neither extreme is healthy. But when you get to a place in life where you are no longer doing the things you love—for example, you used to love to hang out with your family but you no longer do that, you used to love to play Frisbee but you no longer do that, or you used to love to go fly-fishing but you no longer do that—you will begin to see that the lizard brain is very active in you.

The reason is that enjoyment releases certain neurochemicals in our brain—four to be precise—commonly known as "happy chemicals." As we release these happy chemicals by doing things we enjoy, we still the lizard brain, because there is no perceived threat to respond to. Each happy chemical—endorphins, dopamine, oxytocin, and serotonin—is activated in slightly different ways, and produces slightly different feelings, but they all minimize our sensitivity to the things that trigger our lizard brain's responses.

What's interesting is that even though these chemicals are not designed to be always present, but rather to ebb and flow, you can trigger their release, and then extend their effects, by not only doing something enjoyable, but also by both planning it before and then thinking about it after. To give you an example, some people love to travel. I tell such people, always have a trip planned. Likely you can't travel every weekend—or even every month, for that matter. But when *are* you traveling? By putting it on your calendar, not only are you more likely to do it (since you have blocked off the space for it), you will think about it in the meantime. Just thinking about something you're going to do in the future can bring your natural dopamine levels up—and possibly serotonin and oxytocin as well. You can elevate your own neurochemicals. And by doing so, you actually decrease the stress chemical cortisol, which the lizard brain thrives on. Hence, it's a one-two punch.

I have worked with many, many clients who were both astonished and discouraged, when they realized that they weren't doing the things they enjoyed anymore. But as they slowly began to bring those things back in their life—when life was no longer an endless to-do list of chores, but now included things they actually *wanted* to do—they could see the lizard brain getting still, at least in those moments. And if we can still the lizard brain in certain moments, we can then build upon that. So go do something you enjoy!

WELLNESS

The third strategy I promote, and perhaps the least surprising, is physical wellness. I start the discussion of wellness with—again, unsurprisingly—nutrition and exercise. This is one that Jake actually did quite well with, in the story. He and

Laurie both were managing their physical health quite well. But they came to understand this better after their daughter's injury, and seeing its effects, both on her and on the family as a whole. If you, or someone you know, has been injured, lives with chronic pain, or is simply in poor physical condition, you can usually clearly see the lizard brain in action. Being physically unwell simply takes a great deal of energy, which means we have less energy to expend on other things—such as stilling our lizard brain. The better your overall physical health, the more energy you have to manage things so that the lizard brain doesn't have to.

Wellness is the word that I use, partly so we could form our company name (Rewire), but also because it is a concept that involves both nutrition and exercise, which is a great place to start a discussion about general physical health. And these two categories within wellness are areas that most people, I think, are already aware of.

When I start to talk about wellness in our seminars, I often see a lot of eyes glaze over. I think that has to do with how much we already talk about this topic in this country. Think about all the books, magazines, and blogs dedicated to the subject, not to mention discussions on social media, or around the water cooler. There might be as much written about physical health as about any other topic. This is good on the one hand, as it shows we recognize its importance. But it can be bad on the other, in that there is so much information out there, and so much of it conflicting, faddish, or even misleading, that it is easy to get overwhelmed.

I also think that often when we talk about wellness, what we're really talking about is how we fit into the clothes that we wear. It's simply the culture that we live in. But within the context of stilling the lizard brain, and certainly within the confines of this book, the focus is not on what you look like, or whether or not you're happy with how your clothes fit. We only care about how being physically well affects the lizard brain—that is, how exercise and nutrition affect our neurochemistry.

The amount of scientific work that has been done on this is subject is astounding, and is often focused on minute details. Take something like myelin, the viscous substance that surrounds the nerve fibers forming our neural pathways, and you'll find a huge amount of research that explains how our myelin sheaths are affected by what we eat. But that's getting a little too narrowly-focused for our purposes. And it isn't my intention to write a book on the finer details of the connection between neurochemicals and nutrition, or neurochemicals and exercise. There are already plenty of them available if you are interested. So let's take the 30,000-foot overview, and just talk about wellness.

Are you physically well?

If you think being sleep-deprived is a common problem, try asking people about their physical wellness. Most people I talk to, especially business people, know they need to eat better than they're eating, and need to get more exercise than they are getting. And as you may intuit from your own experience, the number one reason people give for not exercising is always a lack of time, at least in the business world. But think of how much time we spend making up for our lack of physical wellness, such as when we have to take sick days or recover from an injury. We would do far better to invest a little in wellness up front, rather than to have to deal with all of the repercussions of not being well, in terms of time alone. But that's too logical for our lizard brain.

There have been many studies recently on the average American worker, and how many work hours are lost due to a lack of wellness. It's a massive amount. The government, insurance companies, and many individual businesses are attempting to change this with various types of wellness programs, to try to encourage changes in behavior. And many people are making some of those changes. But by and large, we still live in an overwhelmingly unhealthy culture.

Maybe by witnessing Jake's life, you'll begin to recognize how being physically well is something that can help still your lizard brain. If instead, you think, "I want to go on a diet to lose weight, in order to look good," that's fine, too. You certainly can—the reason is not really all that important. What is important is that you understand the amount of good neurochemicals you can get from good nutrition and exercise. In other words, you need to be more active, if you want your lizard brain to be less active.

And consider the correlation between wellness and rest. Most people don't need to see the research linking better wellness to good rest in order to make the connection, because it's obvious. After you exert yourself, even if it's just by taking a walk, you get better rest. And better rest results in more energy, which leads to more activity, forming a positive-feedback loop. The two strategies are now working together to still our lizard brain.

People will change under one of three circumstances: (a) they've *heard* something enough times, (b) they've *had* it—they're fed up, or (c) they're *hurt*. I hope that you don't have to get any further than circumstance number one—that this book will have allowed you to finally hear it, that it will be the "enough" that inspires you to make the changes you need to make. Because having to get to the point of being fed up or hurt just makes getting well so much more difficult in the long run. There are countless really great books on nutrition and on how to get physically fit, so we won't spend any time on those subjects here. But please hear it. Move more. Eat better. This is a proven strategy for stilling your lizard brain.

INVEST

The fourth strategy is invest, and it's one that I actually had fun writing about with regard to Jake's life. If you will recall, Jake's wife Laurie signed them up to volunteer at an event with the Special Olympics, committing him to an investment of his time and energy with an unfamiliar group. I wanted him to be real, and to want to protect his weekend. (Maybe there's a little autobiography in that section as well.)

The idea of investing has been an interesting one for us to research, and on this subject, too, there is a tremendous body of work about how learning to give of ourselves benefits our higher-process thinking. But I want to discuss it in the context of the lizard brain. Given that the lizard brain protects survival, it is always trying to get you to cling to what you have, claiming that it will help keep you alive. Whether it is possessions, thoughts, or even time, the lizard brain tells you to hoard it. Don't give it away, because you'll lose it. For this reason, giving to other people is a very unnatural act. Therefore, this strategy of investment as a means of stilling our lizard brain is very counter-intuitive.

Many people say, "I'd like to give more money, but I need to make more of it first." Or, "There just isn't time enough to give some away." But these excuses are never really true. Even as you read this, are you thinking to yourself about all the areas of your life that are impoverished? Or are you thinking that this idea of investing time, money, or resources in other people can't possibly pertain to you, because you simply don't have enough?

The fact is that if you give something away, you teach your brain to think you have a surplus of it. But when you never give anything away, you're effectively teaching your brain that you don't have enough of whatever it is. It's a scarcity mindset versus an abundance mindset. When I work one-on-one with clients and they tell me how little time they have, for example, I will often give them the assignment of giving some time away. And I typically have to work hard to convince them that they truly do have the time to give away, because I'm clearly wrong, right? (There's the right/wrong thing all over again.) But if the client begins to give—even a little, and even if they think they can't afford to—they suddenly start to realize that they have more time than they thought they did.

This explains why there are some people who are incredibly philanthropic, who have time to work at a soup kitchen, and also run three companies during the week. It's inexplicable, unless you realize that they have stilled their lizard brain, which allows them to be that much more productive. When our lizard brain is still, we're far more creative, we're far more productive, and we have energy to take on new things. And it explains how a woman who laundered clothes for other people her whole life (not a terribly high-paying job, especially in rural Mississippi) found a way to donate $150,000, before she died, to finance scholarships.[17]

And so investing with time, investing with money, investing with your expertise, or investing with anything you have to give is a great way to help still the lizard brain. It clearly tells the lizard brain that your survival is not threatened, because you have an abundance.

Learn to be a great giver—giving of your time, giving of your energy, giving of your resources, and giving of yourself. I don't care whom you give to—just give! And remember that learning to give away is learning to give away before you feel like you have enough.

RELEASE

The fifth strategy that Jake uncovered was release. Releasing is actually the art of forgiveness. At the mention of forgiveness, people often wonder if there is a spiritual component to this book. That's not my intention—though of course, forgiveness is a large element in many faith traditions. If it is helpful to tie this to your spiritual beliefs, that's great, but even without a religious element, forgiveness does some really amazing things in our brains. Our intent is to understand how forgiving people is effective in stilling the lizard brain.

When I was creating the six strategies, this one caused me to go back and really consider the "must-be-right" part of the lizard brain. Insisting on being right all the time is effectively giving steroids to your lizard brain. Again, sometimes right over wrong is definitely worth fighting for. The trick here, one that Jake had to learn at his own pace, is how long will we insist on being right, and about which things? I believe it's virtually impossible not to believe you're right about things—that part of the lizard brain is ingrained in each one of us. But like Jake, we need to consider what we might lose if we hold on too tightly to our "rightness."

People hurt people. It happens all the time. And usually we don't think that we do it; that's the "must-be-right" part. We are never the ones at fault. But I promise you, I've hurt people in the things I've said and done. And so have you.

But we can learn to recognize that we're not always right, and ask ourselves some questions, such as: how long will we stay angry with this? And how quickly can we forgive? And we can learn to ask those questions even when we're certain we are right. That is the essence of the practice of metacognition—the practice of thinking about how we're thinking about something.

The more expedient we can be in forgiving—that is, the faster we can absolve the people who have wronged us—the quicker we can still our lizard brain. But I have also come to realize that it isn't always people that need to be forgiven—sometimes it's things, or circumstances. For example, you might be confronted with a costly, unexpected car repair. Or you might get a serious medical diagnosis. The question then becomes: how long will you cling to your anger, frustration, or the feeling of being wronged?

And often, it's not another person or situation we need to forgive—it's ourselves. With Jake, I chose to focus on his need to forgive himself for what happened in his past. Jake had had an addiction. In an effort to keep it buried, he never talked about it. But when he discovered that his friend also had an addiction, his past reared its head again. He had never really let it go. And because he lived with a tremendous amount of guilt, he hadn't been able to move forward. Reading this, you might be starting to realize that the person you need to forgive is actually yourself.

Remember, we're relating forgiveness and this concept of release to how it will be helpful in stilling your lizard brain. So I would invite you to make a list. What is the situation you cannot let go of? And specifically, who are the people that you need to release in life? Yourself, perhaps? Don't underestimate the power of this strategy. Release. Or, in the immortal words of Queen Elsa from the Disney movie *Frozen*, "Let it go!"

EXECUTE

The sixth, and final, strategy that Jake discovers in his story is execute. Execute is unlike the other strategies in that it isn't something specific to do, it's the fact that we are actually taking action. With rest, you can learn to rest your mind, or maximize your sleep quality. With enjoy, you can do things that make you happy. The same is true of being well, investing, and releasing. These are all things that you can do.

Learning to execute isn't a thing you do. It's the doing itself. In reading this book, we're learning, which is good, but it's not enough. It's only when knowledge about the lizard brain is applied that this book will have practical value for the people who read it.

Jake, in his story, had a meltdown and then went through a period where he swore off learning. But in doing so he also effectively swore off *doing*. As he learned about his own lizard brain, and as he learned these strategies to still the lizard brain, he came to a pivotal point. He was certainly already working toward it by trying to get more rest, by going to baseball games with his wife, and by enjoying doing things with his children. But then he came to the point where he realized that the knowledge he had accumulated about how his brain works, and how his lizard brain influenced him, was all theory. He was learning for learning's sake, but there was no manifestation of that learning in his life.

As he understood what the lizard brain was really all about, he finally began to realize that he needed to take action on that understanding. I didn't want to write a fairytale ending where he went off into the sunset, and all was good. Instead, Jake would ultimately learn that these strategies are not things to win and conquer, but rather to pursue and practice.

If you put this book down and think either, "I liked it," or, "I didn't like it," but don't actually do anything, then I haven't achieved my goal. The book wasn't ever intended to be merely hypothetical. While simply knowing more about the lizard brain is great, my intention as the author was that you would be inspired—motivated, enabled, and certainly encouraged—to go *do* something with that knowledge.

And so I end with a question: as you've understood the story, as you've seen how the lizard brain works, and understand the strategies to still it that allow us to transform ourselves, what will you now do? What will you actually go and do?

EPILOGUE (LIZARDLY EVER AFTER)

I TOOK THE ONE LESS TRAVELED BY,
AND THAT HAS MADE ALL THE DIFFERENCE.

—Robert Frost

*

Jake was coming up to the one-year anniversary of the infamous meltdown. He sat at the kitchen counter, enjoying a cup of coffee while he waited for his daughters, and began thinking about these past months of working on his lizard brain.

He was busy at work, and the girls were back in school. Katy's ankle had healed well enough to allow her to play on the school's volleyball team that fall, and she and Kylee were having a great season. He and Laurie had grown closer over the past few months as they enjoyed more date nights, and he was growing increasingly passionate about the Special Olympics. In fact, he had told Laurie he might even take a position on the local board.

Jake and Laurie still found themselves in skirmishes now and then, but both were becoming more able to see themselves wanting to be right, and were better able to see which battles were—and which weren't—worth fighting for. Jake secretly wondered if he would ever completely shake his desire to be right, but generally felt good about how far he'd come. He noticed how it was especially helping his relationship with his daughters.

Perhaps most importantly, Jake and Laurie were able to speak more openly about the past—in particular, about Jake's addiction that had been such a hidden source of pain. Jake was becoming increasingly understanding and patient with himself, and—subsequently—with others. His colleagues noticed this, as did his friends, his daughters, and most importantly, Laurie.

Jake's lizard brain was far from being a place of harmonious peace, however, and he still had his moments of struggle. But he was becoming more aware of what an active lizard brain felt like, and also how he felt when it was still. While continuing to study this part of the brain, Jake had come to understand that success in stilling his lizard brain was just as much about being aware of it as it was about trying to force it to be still.

Awareness had become Jake's new favorite topic. And as he grew in his ability to practice awareness, he came across several articles on the subject. It seemed like everywhere Jake turned, people around him were talking about awareness. Often referred to as mindfulness, the topic was everywhere. One Saturday afternoon, while shopping for a small party he and Laurie were hosting, he noticed that *Time* magazine was doing a cover story on the power of mindfulness at work.[18] This made Jake laugh, because it reminded him how, early in his journey, he couldn't stop seeing (and hearing songs about) lizards.

Now it was mindfulness rather than lizards, but as with the lizard sightings, it all pointed him back to the lizard brain. And he continued to grow in his awareness of how it affected him at any given moment.

Jake realized how far he had come since that seminar a year before. He had felt so hopeless that day because he didn't think he was changing, growing, or becoming a better person, and he had no faith that would ever change. But after this last—albeit often difficult—year of discovery, he had become aware that somewhere along the way, hope had returned.

The sound of pounding feet on the stairs pulled him out of his reverie, and Jake got up to take his family to a baseball game—something they had all come to enjoy. His lizard brain was still with him—but in that moment it was still, and Jake was grateful.

NOTES

1 This will be discussed further later in the book. For now, it's enough to know that the definition for "lizard brain" changes depending on the discipline using the term. It means one thing to psychologists, another to social scientists, another to neurobiologists, and another to herpetologists. Hence Jake finding some seemingly contradictory uses of the term.

2 Phyllis Books, "The Reptilian Brain and How It Can Stop Your Child From Learning," *Moms Everyday Resource* (blog), accessed April 22, 2017, http://www.momseveryday.com/home/health/misc/drbooks-reptilian-brain-166265406.html; Susanne Vogel and Lars Schwabe, "Learning and Memory Under Stress: Implications For the Classroom," *Science of Learning* 1 (2016), accessed May 2, 2017, http://dx.doi.org/10.1038/npjscilearn.2016.11.

3 "Fetal Development: Baby's Nervous System and Brain," *What to Expect* (online), updated July 14, 2017, accessed July 17, 2017, https://www.whattoexpect.com/pregnancy/fetal-brain-nervous-system/. See also Joan Stiles and Terry L. Jernigan,

"The Basics of Brain Development," *Neuropsychology Review* 20, no. 4 (November 2010), accessed June 3, 2017, http://dx.doi.org/10.1007/s11065-010-9148-4. Note that much attention is given to the developments in the prefrontal cortex ("forebrain") and midbrain structures. This is because gestational development of reptilian brain ("hindbrain") structures conclude much earlier than the other two regions of the brain.

4 Timm Rosburg, Axel Mecklinger, and Christian Frings, "When the Brain Decides: A Familiarity-Based Approach to the Recognition Heuristic as Evidenced by Event Related Brain Potentials," *Psychological Science* 22 (December 2011): 1527-1534.

5 Robert A. Burton, *On Being Certain: Believing You Are Right Even When You're Not* (New York: St. Martin's Press, 2008). This is an interesting book from a neurologist looking at how our own belief of being right isn't usually a conscious choice, but functions as basic survival trait.

6 Jonah Lehrer, "Are Emotions Prophetic?" *Wired*, March 1, 2012, accessed April 5, 2017, https://www.wired.com/2012/03/are-emotions-prophetic/.

7 Johanna M. Jarcho, Elliot T. Berkman, and Matthew D. Lieberman, "The Neural Basis of Rationalization: Cognitive Dissonance Reduction During Decision-Making," *Social Cognitive and Affective Neuroscience* 6, no. 4 (September 2011), accessed June 4, 2017, http://dx.doi.org/10.1093/scan/nsq054. There are a number of theories that address this characteristic

of the lizard brain (for example, "post-decision rationalization," or "retrospective sense-making"). But given our interest in the brain, this study is interesting because the researchers were able to view, in real time, what was happening in people's brains as they attempted to justify decisions when they were confronted with contradictory information.

8 Charles Duhigg has a compellingly excellent introduction to this topic in *The Power of Habit: Why We Do What We Do in Life and Business* (New York: Random House, 2014). Excerpts from this work are viewable online—hence Jake coming across the concept in our story. One of the common findings from researchers is that when animals and humans are unable to form habits, life expectancy drops sharply, as in this study looking at the role of the basal ganglia in habit formation and maintenance: Karin Foerde and Daphna Shohamy, "The Role of the Basal Ganglia in Learning and Memory: Insight from Parkinson's disease," *Neurobiology of Learning and Memory* 96, no. 4 (September 2011), accessed online June 16, 2017, http://dx.doi.org/10.1016/j.nlm.2011.08.006.

9 Neel Burton, "Our Hierarchy of Needs: Why True Freedom Is a Luxury of the Mind." *Psychology Today*, May 23, 2012, accessed November 30, 2015, https://www.psychologytoday.com/blog/hide-and-seek/201205/our-hierarchy-needs.

10 Karin Foerde and Daphna Shohamy, "The Role of the Basal Ganglia in Learning and Memory"; Nicola Broadbent, Larry Squire and Robert Clark, "Rats Depend on Habit

Memory for Discrimination Learning and Retention," *Learning & Memory* 14, no. 3 (March 2007), http://dx.doi.org/10.1101/lm.455607.

11 Amie M. Gordon and Serena Chen, "The Role of Sleep in Interpersonal Conflict," *Social Psychological and Personality Science* 5, no. 2 (May 2013), accessed online September 9, 2016, http://dx.doi.org/10.1177%2F1948550613488952.

12 William D.S. Killgore et al., "Sleep Deprivation Reduces Perceived Emotional Intelligence and Constructive Thinking Skills," *Sleep Medicine* 9, no. 5 (July 2008): 517-26.

13 US Department of Health and Human Services, Centers for Disease Control and Prevention, National Center for Health Statistics, *Prescription Sleep Aid Use Among Adults: 2005-2010*, NCHS Data Brief no. 127: August 2013, accessed online April 30, 2016, https://www.cdc.gov/nchs/data/databriefs/db127.pdf.

14 A good jumping-off point for psychological and neurological effects of rest (sleep especially) is neuroscientist Penelope Lewis' *The Secret World of Sleep: The Surprising Science of the Mind at Rest* (New York: St. Martin's Press: 2013).

15 Related to the effects of alcohol on sleep, see the literature review from Irshaad Ebrahim et al., "Alcohol and Sleep I: Effects on Normal Sleep," *Alcoholism, Clinical & Experimental Research* 37, no. 4 (April 2013): 539-549.

16 On the issue of the "blue light waves" and sleep, this interview with two neuroscientists provides a good overview of the research: Jessica Schmerler, "Q&A: Why Is Blue Light before Bedtime Bad for Sleep?" *Scientific American*, September 1, 2015, accessed May 3, 2016, https://www.scientificamerican.com/article/q-a-why-is-blue-light-before-bedtime-bad-for-sleep/.

17   Oseola McCarty, Hattiesburg, Mississippi. 1908-1999.

18   "The Mindful Revolution," *Time*, February 3, 2014.

ACKNOWLEDGMENTS

Thank you to all who had a hand in this.

Acknowledgment pages are interesting things. To be honest, I have often skipped over them, believing that the real "meat" of what I want to read is in the body of the book. I have often been too impatient, longing to get to the heart of the matter. Why is it important to know (or care) about someone's desire to recognize someone else? Well, now that the shoe is on the other foot, I understand why it's important. In fact, I have recently begun to go back to some of my favorite books just to read the acknowledgments, and I am coming to see the acknowledgments as necessary for giving credit where credit is due. Acknowledgments also give the reader a glimpse into the heart of the author—something I am finding more and more relevant to any written work.

My wife, Raffa, who so patiently read through this story with me several times. I can't even imagine how many times she must have bitten her own lip knowing that Jake was, in part, the man she married. How much of this story is an autobiographical? Please don't ask Raffa. Her lip must have her permanent teeth marks on it already.

Stephanie Wetherby has been an incredible editor-in-chief. I couldn't have done this without her. Her creativity, patience, diligence, and fastidiousness have made it all possible. Jake's life would never have made the pages without her. Thanks for getting him out of bed, Steph! By the way, some of her is in him, too!

To my children who have endured my lizard brain all these years, I thank you.

Special thanks to Steve Longan for his dedication to the research that Jake uncovered. Also thanks to my partner at Rewire, Jason Abell, without whom the company would have never made it off the ground.

To all my clients, who will doubtless come to a particular section and feel either proud or annoyed that I wrote about them, may you find peace in stilling your inner lizard.

Finally, for the presence of the Divine in my life. To offer a dedication to God seems a bit silly to me—since my hope is that my whole existence acts as one big dedication to Him. I hope, one day, to ask why He created the lizard brain the way He did. In the meantime, I'll keep doing my best to be still, and to know that He is God.

ABOUT THE AUTHOR

Steve is the Founder and CEO of Rewire, Inc., a company born out of his passion to help people succeed through understanding how the human mind shapes the path to success. His focus is on bringing current neurological discoveries to bear in areas of leadership, management, sales and operational performance, interpersonal communication, improved corporate culture, and personal excellence, and his goal is to make the science behind how the human brain works applicable to how we manage our day-to-day lives. You can find Steve at www.rewireinc.com.

TRANSFORMATION FROM THE INSIDE OUT

ACHIEVE
AUTHENTIC, SUSTAINABLE CHANGE
BY LEARNING HOW
TRANSFORMED THINKING
LEADS TO TRANSFORMED ACTIONS.

Rewire offers **workshops** and **keynotes**, **GroupWire Forums** (role-oriented group coaching), **OneWires** (individual coaching), and customized **Corporate Programs**, all aimed at helping you and your company bring about radical growth.

Visit us at **www.rewireinc.com** or reach out to us directly at **grow@rewireinc.com** or by phone at **503-741-2288**.

THE
LIZARD QUIZ
YOUR BRAIN MAY BE HOLDING YOU BACK!

The Lizard Brain looks for **familiarity**.

The Lizard Brain insists on **being right**.

The Lizard Brain establishes **habits**.

The Lizard Brain wants to **control**.

Do you know which of these four characteristics is strongest in you?

Take the LIZARD QUIZ today!

www.lizardquiz.com

Made in the USA
Las Vegas, NV
11 February 2021

17623647R00100